6/2q

VOICES ON THE GREEN

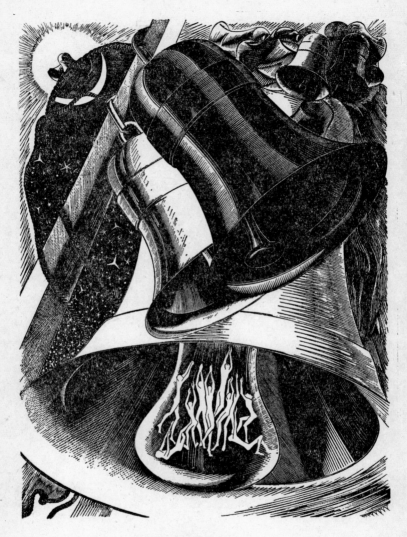

JOY BELLS

Blair Hughes Stanton

VOICES
on the
GREEN

★

Edited by

A. R. J. WISE
and
REGINALD A. SMITH

" When the voices of children are heard on the green
And laughing is heard on the hill."
WILLIAM BLAKE

MICHAEL JOSEPH LTD.
26 *Bloomsbury Street, London, W.C.1*

FIRST PUBLISHED 1945

Set and printed in Great Britain by Sherratt and Hughes, the St. Ann's Press, Altrincham, in Granjon 11 on 12 point, and bound by James Burn.

CONTENTS

*

WOOD
ENGRAVINGS

★

TAILPIECES

★

By K. J. H. CRADDOCK (pp. 13, 17, 67, 69, 193, 222) and titlepieces; CARISSIMA FONTAINE (p. 174); ROBERT GIBBINGS (pp. 62, 117, 205); ERIC KING (p. 146); CLAIRE LEIGHTON (pp. 90, 95); AGNES MILLER PARKER (p. 124); JOHN O'CONNOR (pp. 104, 189); MARGARET PILKINGTON (p. 30); ERNEST SELLERS (p. 166); CLIFFORD WEBB (p. 44).

ACKNOWLEDGMENTS

★

Henry Williamson's story is from *Tales of a Devon Village* (Faber & Faber); Gerald Bullett's story is from *Twenty-four Tales* (J. M. Dent & Sons); and A. P. Herbert's poem is from *She-Shanties* (Ernest Benn). The frontispiece, by Blair Hughes Stanton, is reproduced by permission of the B.B.C.; Claire Leighton's engravings (pp. 90 and 95) by permission of Victor Gollancz. The engravings by Robert Gibbings are included by permission of Hodder & Stoughton (p. 62), J. M. Dent & Sons (p. 205) and the Golden Cockerel Press (p. 117), who have also given permission to reproduce the engraving by Eric Ravilious (p. 14). The blocks were made by Northern Photo Engraving Company.

PRE-NATAL

IT was the long tradition behind Saint Mary's Hospitals of Manchester that inspired the conception of *Voices on the Green*. It is a tradition that has brought together the rigid impersonality and austerity of science and a world of love, the tenderness of motherhood, the warmth and laughter of happy homes, and yet again the shadows that neither man's devotion nor his skill can utterly dispel.

It was our thought that this tradition, emerging from a glorious and fruitful past into a future of still more hopeful endeavour, might make appeal to those who have the gift of words and that they might fashion for us a " monument more lasting than brass " to this moment in the pageant of motherhood and childhood. So we wrote to them :

". . . because we think you may like to contribute to a miscellany of high literary and artistic standard. The book will be linked with the work of Saint Mary's Hospitals for Women and Children, Manchester—the largest foundation of its kind in the country, with maternity, gynaecological and children's departments and medical teaching in these subjects. Although the profits are to be devoted to the funds of these hospitals the primary purpose of the book is to deepen and spread a general appreciation of the needs of mothers and children, and of the family as a unit of society.

The authors and artists whose contributions appear in the book will not necessarily address themselves directly to this theme; our suggestion is that, submitting themselves to its inspiration, they should contribute some piece of their own kind of creative work—whether it be verse, a story or an essay lightly celebrating some chosen aspect or treating some problem of social life for which the writer feels particular concern. We picture the cumulative whole as an artistic unity, a little loosely held together perhaps, but rich in variety of substance and manner and sharing the same broad inspiration . . ."

And we were not disappointed. Authors and artists are generous souls. We were in the fifth year of war, everybody was tired, and paper rationing had made great difficulties for the professional writer, but despite all this, between thirty and forty authors

7

responded with enthusiasm and readily placed their art and skill at the disposal of a ' proposal so excellent ', a ' project so interesting '.

Now that all their contributions are brought together we believe the sensitive reader will be impressed with the way in which each has helped in building up for this literary monument a definite shape of its own. The book ' flows ' like the lines of good sculpture. It goes forward from one emphasis to another, with crescendos that mount and spend themselves, before moving on to state a new aspect of the theme.

First, Mr. Spender sings of the intimate mystery of beginnings, and the note is sustained in Miss Bowen's delicate vignette and in a group of love stories of unusual originality and gentleness. Next, Miss Sackville-West's poem suggests the tremulous joy that comes when the children are born and we learn what they may cost in concern and sorrow. The shadowed charm of Mr. Tomlinson's elusive meditation on " The Little Things " extends the field of the note of tenderness. Then, with Mr. Edmund Blunden's " Voices I Heard " we re-enter the fairyland we had outgrown or forgotten. Sometimes the picture is still of childhood as it looks to us but soon the child's own standpoint takes control.

The final movement is into the future, and its farthest vistas appear in the beautiful mystical poem by Miss Margaret Kennedy, with its confidence in the triumph yet to come through the Seed of the Woman. In the meantime there are stern reminders of war, Mr. Priestley's idyll of the beauty that life might be, and some fantastic hints of what it may become if we don't watch out! We may find allegory in Miss Bottome's story of a childish mind in a powerful frame. In the end it all returns to our own hearths, with Miss Viola Meynell reminding us in moving verse of our own vital responsibility, of how much the children look to us, and how easily we may destroy their hope and trust and mar the designs on which the happiness and fullness of their life depends.

Our debt is not only to the authors and artists. We are also deeply grateful to the publishers, Messrs. Michael Joseph, and to the printers, Messrs. Sherratt and Hughes, whose generosity has enabled the entire profits of this book to be devoted to Saint Mary's Hospitals.

—THE EDITORS

Stephen Spender

THE CHILD

"YOU dream," he said, "because of the child
    Asleep in the nest of your entrails, whose dreams
Flutter through your blood in streams."

"Baby," her lips dreamt, and he smiled.

He laid his head, weighed with a thought
On the sleep of her lips. Thus locked
Within the lens of their embrace
They watched the life their lives had wrought,
The folded future active street
With walls of flesh and crowing face,
Within her flesh complete,
Between their clinging bodies rocked.

Marjorie Bowen

THE SWEET CHESTNUT TREE

TWO children ran out from the wood on the hillside; they carried each a small rough basket filled full with sweet chestnuts; the little girl fell and spilled her treasures, and, in searching for them, her eager feet trampled a chestnut into the warm, dark earth.

That was in Spain, five hundred years ago.

The chestnut, some years afterwards, had grown into a noble tree, standing alone on the slope of the hill; children played beneath it, tossing about the heavy shining fruit, or sleeping beneath the dense shade of the wide branches of golden leaves, which sheltered them like the arms, robe and flowing hair of a gracious and gentle lady; all the children greatly loved the chestnut tree.

In time, a woodman set his axe to the tree; he was a grandson of the little maiden who had dropped the chestnut from which it had sprung; she had now grown to a very old woman. Children stood round, sad and grieved to see the yellow tresses of the tree crash down. Some monks from the monastery bought the tree from the woodman. They were building a church so large that the children were frightened of it; peering through the vast dark doorway they felt timid and very small.

A wood-carver saw the tree brought to the cathedral; now it was a log, bound like a prisoner behind two beautiful white oxen.

"I will have that for my statue," he said; so the log was drawn to his workshop in the shadow of the church; the children pressed round the entrance, curious, silent, while he worked.

He declared that his labour was oddly light; not as if he were designing and carving a figure, but releasing a spirit; under his quick and able hands the shape of a beautiful woman came out of the log; she held out her arms, her robe and hair flowing into a protective shelter; she looked down smiling. As a painter coloured her hair golden, her face rosy, and her robe brown, as the tree had been, the children clapped their hands.

Some workmen carried the statue into the church with great ceremony—"Holy Mary, Queen of Heaven, Madonna of the Sweet Chestnut Tree," they called her; the monks found her a crown of spiky silvery stars and a necklace of gold lace.

The children were no longer timid, and crept into the great church and knelt before the statue which always smiled; she soothed them when they were cross, cured them of their ills, found their lost toys, and kept their secrets; round the shrine hung little silver models of babies she had healed, pets she had saved, dolls she had repaired—all offered in thanksgiving.

For many, many years she stood there smiling; when the smoke of the candles dimmed her robe it was repainted, when her diadem became dulled and worn they re-crowned her; always the children pressed round her, not afraid to laugh and sleep at her feet; and it seemed with the years that she stooped lower towards them with a wider sweep of her protecting arms.

One sad winter day the statue stood desolate and alone; the candles were gutted out, and thick dust lay in the folds of her robe; she smiled sadly into the darkness, for even the sacred lamps before the High Altar were extinguished. Monks who had tended the great church and the children had all fled, for there was war in the land; foreign soldiers tramped through the snow, cold, ragged, hungry. They had entered the cathedral and pried about it; it was very cold; some of them were wounded, some had bare feet; they had marched all day through a bitter storm.

A party of them cut down the statue of the Queen of Heaven, carried her outside, then built up a heap of straw and sticks from the monastery, and placed her on the fire; that terrible winter there was a great scarcity of wood.

The golden hair blended with the flames as the statue burnt, the brown robe changed to sparkles of red and blue, the rosy face smiled from the heart of the fire; the ragged soldiers, bleak and haggard, all gathered round; never had they felt such kind, such generous warmth, which seemed to bring a blessing with it; seated round the huge blaze, sad and tired, the men dreamed and saw visions of thousands of little children playing in the flames.

While the soldiers slept, huddled in their cloaks, the fire sank down; when in the cold morning the soldiers had departed, and their bitter march was continued through the snow, the heart of the chestnut tree lay cold amid the ashes heaped outside the deserted church.

In the springtime a peasant crept back to his deserted home, and soon the old monks returned to the desolate church; the snow had melted, the ashes blown away, but a stump of wood marked the place of the fire where the soldiers had bivouacked.

" Just what I want to make a cradle with," said the peasant; for he had a very small sick baby.

The wood was scooped out into the shape of a little bed, rounded and set on rockers; everyone was very poor because of the war, but the monks found an old woollen robe with which to line the cradle. The poor baby became well and happy; he was always smiling. The father said the cradle had brought luck, and the mother said the boy had a guardian saint, for she had surely seen a tall woman, sweetly smiling, with golden hair and brown robe, holding the baby on her knees, so like the Madonna of the Sweet Chestnut Tree she remembered in the old church.

Soon the peasant prospered; the sacred lamps were lit again before the High Altar of the cathedral; the young monks rebuilt the monastery; a beautiful alabaster statue of the Queen of Heaven, gilded and painted, was set up where the carved chestnut tree had stood.

Years went on, and many children had been rocked in the cradle. One day a young man said : " We will buy another cradle for little Jose; that is very old and mean."

So the ancient cradle was chopped up and cast on the kitchen fire; but grandfather, remembering he had made it, and what his good wife had said, snatched a brand of it from the flames and carved a little puppet that moved its arms and legs; and grandmother made a tiny brown robe and hair of yellow wool.

Children played with the doll the old people had fashioned, until clothes, limbs and head were pulled off and lost.

A small boy wanted to try his first knife; he hacked a bowl no bigger than his hand out of the body of the doll.

His sister took it from him; it was her birthday, and a warm happy autumn morning. She said : " I will plant my chestnut in that—the big chestnut that is beginning to burst."

They put dark earth around the chestnut and hid it in the bowl; but their mother told them when the green leaves appeared the seedling must be planted in the open.

The children dug a hole in the hillside near the church and buried the bowl and the chestnut, which had become one.

When they were grown up and came home after many happenings, they found a sweet young chestnut tree growing alone on the hillside, with many children asleep under its golden boughs.

THE HANSOM CAB

Eric Ravilious

Lance Sieveking

REVOLVING DOOR

A BABY is a jolly thing
  All curly from the womb,
So let us many get and bring
  In case we early to the tomb
Should be abruptly called.

This way for the Early Tombs! This way for the Early Tombs!
No tickets needed, Mam, nor never will I 'ope,
Pass along there, please, straight on down that dark slope,
  This way for the Early Tombs!

  A baby is a curly thing,
    It makes its mother happy;
  It pops, and nips its teething ring
    When daddy changes nappy.
  Ha-Ha! Across its mobile face
    A skelter of emotions race,
  Terror: then giddy joy: then pain:
    Astonishment: then fear again.
     Ecstatic grin
    Tongue out tongue in.
  Round and round and round they go
    Until a solemn gaze on Toe
     Is concentrate.
    Toe: that Great Mystery,
    The Other End of Me!
     Wait. . . .

Another toe!
Pure ecstasy!

Give it a name—a name! This child a name!
  The end and the beginning
    See society spinning
      Spinning society
      Appetite satiety
  The end and the beginning
  Are very much the same.

North and south and east and west
The baby only knows that best
Of all things in the world is Breast;
Item : one object, warm and smooth as silk,
Round and resilient and full of milk,
Questions not 'Whence? Nor not yet wanting 'Hence!'
  O! Would some power the giftie gie us,
  The little niftie thriftie giftie,
    The gift of continence.

There comes a time in every life of every one of us
  When we, because our moment is not ripe,
Pause and regress, and recollect and stumble,
  And then remuster, each in his own type.
And if at such an instant, one should question
  Whether a certain quality should be
Again included in the ego's make-up,
  Again that acorn should bring forth that tree :
Then you may know that time o'er past is wasted;
  That sorrow and strain must be again once more;
That virtue and pride were not completely tasted;
  That sleep had borne you past the precious door.

Close not your eyes, my friend, and not again be cheated,
Lest inattention in the end has you defeated.

A baby is a jolly thing
    Still dusty from the tomb,
So let us many get and bring
    In case we early to the womb
Should be abruptly called.

Thomas Moult

THE ROMANCE OF ROSIE

PROUD as a paycock was my Faither over his little love story, and terrible partickler how and when he told it. For he was a whimsical old manalive, and it was only in wicked weather like this of to-night, when the wind was lord of the moorland and everything indoors safe and cosy, that we could coax it out of him. He would tell us that on such a day, such a night, my Mother first comed into his bachelor-man's life, till he felt he was walking up to heaven in silver slippers, nor knowing if it was on his head he walked instead of his toes and heels.

Therefore he picked always for the telling of his story the times akin to that other blessed time, and then it would break from his lips all queer indeed, and most like a fairytale; but he gave his word 'twas true as gospel. And true as gospel it must have been, for no man at all could make up out of his own thinking-parts a lie so pretty.

Fifty years ago there comed from Lunnon town a strange old fella to spend his summertime in a gamekeeper's hut on these hills of ours. A brokken-down and deserted place it was, and in a lonesome spot, so no wonder the folk hereabouts thought him hardly less than cracked and crazy.

But after a while they got to understand him better, thanks to Polly Staffert, a wench who went up to set his things to rights each day, and when Polly was back in the village again she had a lot of things to tell about—hair-raising things for sartain-sure, and everybody began to respect that old ancient summat wonderful. So curious were the bits she told of, they whispered one to another he must be a wizard-man for sartain-sure. People belonging to my Faither's young life had no more sense than they should have had, 'specially as there warsn't no school-boards to knock nonsense into the thickest yead like they do in these enlightened generations.

Of course, he was one of they *scientific* men, if the dear souls round about had but known it. And because they did not know it they chatted like skeered childer about the manner in which he spent the hours of night-time, when respectable Christians lay abed. For Polly she had told them how he would sit in the dark, staring and staring and staring through a tube-thing at the stars till they seemed so big as little moons. Mighty clever she said he was, because he would promise what the weather was going to be, wet or fine or middling, by peeping down into a tiny box instead of looking skyward.

And yes, what's more, the wire he got some workmen from the towns to stretch high up from that gamekeeper's hut of his for miles and lots of miles over hills and dales and villages made everybody scrat their yeads a tidy bit. It talked out to him from nowhere at all, and in a way he could understand complete, and that's the truth. Polly she said she had heard it set agate a-talking many and many a morning, she had so, yes indeed.

"Tick, tick, ticketty tick," that's what and that's all, yet the old wizard-man told Polly Staffert it was about big happen-ings a hundred miles away and more, and she believed him.

Now, on the moorside in a farm cottage nestling snug, a wench called Rosie Rendle lived along with her mother. A lonely, shivery place you would have thought Old Shiloh for a widder-woman and her darter. The sun never shone there, the very walls seemed to be hiding summat creepy . . . but when the wind comed rushing in that lordly way of his down from the moors and high hilltops the fir trees bent their tall heads together and twined their sheltering arms round the cottage till the storm passed away . . . just to keep Rosie safe, so my

Faither always said and would have us know for sartain-sure. And in the morning those fir trees straightened up again and drew their branches aside and let the sun steal through and wakken her with a kiss.

Rosie Rendle was in truth a bonny lass, and the sun and the fir trees they loved her.

But few human folk knew how bonny she was till after she got wedded, which was not yet awhile, nor shall be till the end of my Faither's love story. Into the villages Rosie went fewer times than seldom, so she never seed the youngish males such as thee, lad (that's what he said to me, he did indeed); and when she happened ever to go villageward her mother made her brush her gold hair back from her forehead and plait it stiff, like thowd mare's tail, and dress so she looked as plain as plain, like thowd woman herself.

Maybe 'twas thoughts of a lonesome hearth bothered that mean female's noddle and made her wishful for to keep Rosie by her own side to the end of her mortal breath. Selfish and all that are widder-females in general, and cruel often as well. They dunnot allow for the dreams which set a young maid standing awesome on the threshold of golden days and golden nights, and lift her hungry heart a-crying to another hungry heart somewhere as she knows nowt about like a peewit cries to her unseen mate in the moondawn.

But there was one of Rosie's pretty ways that all the widder's schemings could not keep hidden for ever. She might tell her to shut her red lips tight across her white teeth when somebody comed nigh, and to hide her dimples out of sight and suchlike, but that girl's voice could not have been kept silent by all the lone widder-women in the world.

A lovely voice it was, and sweet as ringing bells. Sometimes, when Rosie sang on the hillside, the simple ones in the valley would harken, bethinking themselves they listened to a special angel singing at the Throne.

Now Rosie and the ancient wizard-man had met each other,

and they growed into great friends. One day, just before the
Tideswell fair came round—for it was held in the year-fall at
that time of history and not as now in summer—the wizard-
man rose up in the dawnlight and took his legs for a walk
down the moorside to watch the shadders steal away from the
hills. A long mile and more that walk was, and a glorious
morning surely, and soon his sight was blinking a mighty often,
what with the bird music and his memories.

At last he comed to a turn of the footpath where he could
see the red fires of morning touch all the High Peak to colour
so the river Noe ran like a flame. And there, sitting lonely by
a pool at the edge of the lane, nigh to her mother's farm at
Old Shiloh, was Rosie Rendle.

It was a great and grand sight for the old man, I do assure
you.

But what's all this? Instead of the smile that always gave
the wizard his welcome, Rosie's face was all gloom, and tear-
drops, yes indeed, were clinging to her eyes, silver-sweet. Silver-
sweet and no wonder, they being Rosie's tear-drops. And that
old ancient he thought to himself how he would have kissed
them away without any by-her-leave had he been but a thousand
years younger.

" It is early you have rose up, Granfer," said she, for she had
no school-board larning in her speeches hadn't Rosie. But she
had a kind lady's way without needing to larn it, and she made
a curtsey and tried to look nothing but glad.

Thowd man had seen her unhappiness all the same, or he
was a fool and no wizard. So he axed, very gently : " What is
the matter with my little one? It is grieving to me to find a
shadder on your face, Rosie. Let an oldish man sweep it away
like the sun is sweeping away the last darkness of the night."

But Rosie was shy even before her ancient friend, and it was
long and tooked a deal of coaxing before she could persuade
herself to speak her trouble.

" O granfer!" she cried at last, " I am wishful for to see the fair next week at Tidsa. My mother she says I may go, but I have gotten no nice clothes to wear, and my mother says we canna buy any, being so poor, although there be dresses fit for a king's maiden showing in Master Needham's shop-window at Chapel-Frith, and—and——"

Suddenly her eyes had turned to the watter twinkling in the stream at her feet, and her face went all blushes.

". . . And my mother she says none of the young fellas shall be wishful for to dance with me, and—and——"

"Dang your mother for a female with blinded spectacles!" Either dang or maybe bless her was what he said, anyway, and he meant them both, wishing once again in his secret heart that he himself was still a skittish young colt. "But why does she speak like that, little one?"

"Because—because I canna talk and laugh with them like the other girls, so she says. My heart it goes all fluttery if a young fella even looks at me, and I can find no word to say at all, so I do be agreeing with my mother I had better stay at home."

"Come, come," the old man answered, tipping up her chin till she was obliged to gaze into his cheery face a-twinkle; and before his speech had gone far she was smiling out of big eyes as well. "You shall go to the fair sure enough," he said, "and there will be a troop of young fellas waiting to dance with you and ready to hate each other and lose their immortal souls for your sake, for I myself shall arrange it, I do assure you.

"And I will lend you a silver belt to wear, my little one, and you shall look so fine that my wisdom tells me the bravest, bestest young fella in all the countryside shall ax you to dance with him and be most proud and glad all over him even should you say him nay—which you shall not, no, not on your pretty life, so long as that voice of yours can speak one lovely word all by itself."

"Can Nay ever be a lovely word, granfer?"

"A hag herself might be a lovely woman to a youngish male

in his springtime were his heels kept kicking," he answered,
and Rosie did not understand a single word of it, which maybe
was as well, or it might have stayed her from jumping up with
a little laugh of delight. The wizard-man was now stooping
by the pool and he picked up a stone all marked pretty with
coloured stains. Then he told her a bit of story about the
stone, so clever that she forgot to thank him, and he chuckled
to see her hurry away. Off he went after that, up the moorside
and off to his own gamekeeper's hut.

There, standing at the door, awaiting his coming, was a
young fella with a sheepdog to heel. "Bless my avocation and
my life!" exclaimed the wizard-man. "Indeed it is a blighted
morning for all my friends, seemingly. What a long dark
distance you must have carried a face like that. Does the world
trouble you also, my son?"

Sure enough the young man's looks were long as a Methody's
fiddle. On other days his eyes flashed with blue wings, and
laughter lay on his lips, merry as a lark's song. But on this
partickler day he had not even the heart to wonder what the
old wizard meant by asking does the world trouble you *also*,
my son.

Tall and straight and good to meet was Peter Hyde, and a
favourite with all the village where he lived, and a shining
hero to the maidens and no less than a shining hero, though
he cared little or naught for them in return; which may have
been good sense in a young fella, and may have been less.

Peter Hyde was a shepherd under Rushup Edge. He talked
with his dogs as likeably as to humans, choosing always to
spend his days in sunlight on the warm moor, supping his
thirst away at the trickling pools when the summer noon was
hot, lying betwixt the heather and the rushes in the dewy night
and harkening to the call of the pheasants and watching with
high soul the moon waxing bright on the hilltops.

That is the sort of man that Peter was.

"Come, grandfaither, and listen to me if you please," said

Peter. " I have gotten something ticklish to be telling you, and if any man can help me it is you alone. It is for that and nothing else I have come this almighty distance."

The old man nodded. Silently he brought out a chair from the hut and sat in his doorway to listen.

" My trouble is like this," began the young shepherd. " Yon owd mother of mine, bless her dear soul, has axed me many a time to set agate thinking of somebody's darter and fetching her to our home to be a darter to her and for myself a wedded wife. Sir, I hope I make it all plain. . . . And my answer has been after this fashion : ' It shall happen when I find a young woman so good as you, Mother.' But yesterday night she said, very quiet like : ' Peter lad, I am grown old and feeble, and no longer can I mend thy clothes nor keep our hearth clean and tidy. It is fully time thou hadst gotten thyself a wedded wife. So promise me thou wilt goo to Edale Fair a fortneet come Saturday and pick a lass from all the lasses there for festival.'

" What could I say to that, granfer, except promise the old lady what she wished, so feeble she was, so worried moreover? And it weighs heavy on my mortal soul this morning. I can think of naught else, I canna even count sheep ezacally, and the more I try to think and count the heavier and mazier grow my senses. That is why I have come to you, granfer. Can you, with all your knowledge and the fear of God, help me to choose a good wench for to make my mother a darter and myself a wedded wife? "

Now did ever an old man smile and set agate with scratting of his thinking parts as if he knew nothing, nothing whatsoever, like that old man did, lump of ancient mischief that he was!

" What sort of maiden, Peter, are you wishful for to meet? "

" A living thing," said Peter readily, " with a heart like heaven's gold and a way of life like the spring stars have got as they go sparkling through the dusk into the pools of midnight. A maiden who can gather thoughts from the hills and flowers and sky as well as from pots and pans——"

"And from pots and pans as well as from the hills and flowers and sky," put in the old ancient.

"Aye, indeed, and a woman of sense," went on Peter, "with a temper a bit, maybe, but sweet like scalded milkpails . . ."

He stopped of a sudden, surprised at himself, and fearing lest he might be thought wishful for too much altogether. But the old man was nodding his head and smiling as if he wanted to hear more, so the lad set agate again.

". . . sweet as scalded milkpails, and able to cook and mend decently, yet not be cooking and mending till no room is left for me and the gladsome things. My good comrade on the moors and in the valleys she must be, and I her good comrade also; and we shall be naught less than the whole of life to each other till the day of it has gone and we bow ourselves before the darksome night of death."

Peter's eyes they shone like the Almighty was beaming down at him from a window, and the wizard knew with great sureness that Peter was the fit and proper man for Rosie Rendle.

"It is the pick of the basket you want, without a doubt," said he, admiring Peter from head to foot. "And let me tell you, Peter, you have a lucky star, for one such maiden there is for sartain-sure.

"But," the old man wagged his finger, "you shall never find her at Edale fair. 'Twill be at Tideswell she is, next week, not a fortnight off, and though it is a tidy distance for you to travel, you must not fail.

"And," said he, "for fear you do not find her when you get there, you shall come to me on the day before, so I may give you a charm that I will prepare for you, to guide her to your heart."

He bowed his head, like such wise critters do in story-books, and turned back into his hut. As for Peter, he went away thinking what a miracle-man that wizard was for sure, yes indeed.

The young shepherd returned on the appointed morning and received the charm. It was a curious ring, and the old man bade him put it on his finger on the fair-day and wear it pointing to his palm.

" It is a magic ring," said he, " and the magic shall not work unless it is fixed right side up. Before you reach the fair it must be on your finger, and you must dance with every maiden you meet, be she never so shy and humble. When you put your arm about the waist of the wench whose heart is the truest and sweetest and bestest your hand will cling round her as though it never would leave go; and by that sign you shall be guided."

Peter marvelled mightily.

He thanked the wizard-man as he had thanked no human critter ever before, and when the Tideswell fair began he slipped the ring on his finger just as he was bidden.

So did Peter Hyde set out on his quest for the maiden whose heart was the truest and sweetest and bestest.

A big rally of queerish thoughts comed rushing to his yead, and he was all on fire to think his thread would be tangled past all unravelling before the morning sun glittered again across the Derbyshire Peak.

And now for Rosie Rendle. She hovered timidly alongside her mother all the afternoon, shrinking from the haughty glances of the wenches who were not timid at all, no indeed. Rosie was dressed so plain as potato-pie, and her loveliness was all hidden—everything was hidden except the loveliness of that old wizard's silver belt.

" For why did *thee* come to the fair, for why ? " That's what one pert Tidsa female axed poor Rosie. " Didst reckon as some young fella might be wishful for to dance with a mouse to-day, Rosie Rendle ? "

" Well, well," laughed another, more kindly, seeing the

quick flushes on Rosie's face. " You can at least watch our good times."

" But what a lovely belt you've gotten on!" exclaimed a third female. " Where from did you borrow it, Rosie Rendle? "

Rosie's mother dragged her away at that, calling over her shoulder how they were a batch of impudence and the wizard-man gave it to Rosie if they wanted to know so partickler.

Under the trees they went and sat themselves, did Mrs. and Miss Rose Rendle-as-was. For a long time they watched the people dancing, and they harkened to the fiddler's tunes. The afternoon went on and on and sunset comed and then twilight comed as the copper and gold broke up and fell all to bits and pieces in the western heaven. Blind man's holiday it was then, as the old folk used to say, a-laying of their knitting aside when evening walks into the parlour and puts a hand before their eyes.

Rosie sat close to her mother, her head drooping sadly, for no man at all had axed her to dance, and, poor thing, she began to reckon that her best friend the old scientific man had done her a trick and a wrong.

Well, to come back to Peter. He danced with wench after wench, and was honest enough for evermore to confess that he enjoyed every moment—*but* . . . he always added that " but ", especially when someone special—and I mean Someone Very Special—was listening. Peter was not the lad to lack tip-toe partners on the green, stranger though he was in that part of the universe. All the same, he watched sharply for the sign the old man had sworn would come to him. But the grey colours crawled over hearth and heaven, and a mighty wind sprang up, whinnying like Faither's old mare Liddy, and the tree-tops rocked till the lamps of the fair-ground danced like wildish glowworms.

"I be puzzled," he muttered to himself at last, " I be puzzled. Here have I danced with them all, bar only yonder wee thing sitting shy beside her ugly owd mother. I be a-feared of such a watchdog. Surely my friend of the ancient wisdom did not wish me to leap such a terrible obstacle for the sake of one more maiden?"

Then he thought: "But, no; I promised him I would be sartain-sure to dance with every one of 'em, and dance with every one of 'em I shall and the devil take the consequence. So here goes; I shall axe that small mouse immediate."

And he did so. He larnt the name of the small mouse through the aid of another lass, and he went up to her mother and gived such a handsome sweep of a bow to the old woman that she was back in ancient memories all of a sudden, and thinking herself a womanly woman once more, and she had no heart to bar this fine young fella from switching over to Rosie and saying: "Rosie, wilt dance a turn with me, if it please thee?"

Rosie she thrilled from head to foot and back again. The wizard's words were coming true after all!

Could this be the youngish man who according to that good ancient would be glad to dance with her—glad even though she might say him Nay, so long as she gave him some sort of answer?

Little fear of that Nay there was for Peter Hyde, all the same! . . . Indeed she was on her feet to him as quickly as any of those forward wenches had been, lest he should change his mind. Lifting her beautiful eyes to his, she smiled the answer he expected. But he had not expected to see her face was shining more than all the lamps of the fair and the swinging stars.

Into the dance went Peter with his latest partner, and round and about her little silvery waist went Peter's arm. Of course his fingers touched that special belt, just as the wizard-man promised, and in no-way could he take them away again, particularly one finger. . . . Somehow he knew in that very one instant he had found his mother a darter and himself a sweetheart. As they two went dancing in and out, in and out, the other dancers and the watching wallflowers beheld a wondrous transformation in the shy maiden who lived with Widder Rendle at Old Shiloh farm on Kinderside.

A wondrous transformation without a doubt. But her friend the wizard-man would not have thought it more than natural, like all his other *scientific* deeds and discoveries. Her hair was catched up in the wind and shook itself free of the stiffish plaits and spread round her like a glittering kerchief stitched and hemmed all golden. Her eyes shone brightsomely, and her voice rang out laughing from her blessed lips, clear and sweet like the valley folk had heard it in song oftentimes and fancied they harkened to a special angel singing at the Throne. . . .

When the dancing comed to its finish Peter he guided her away from the fair and its bustle into the shadow of the trees that rocked in the wind. There in the shadow of the trees he stood silent a while and looked down into her white, happy face.

" Rosie," said he, very quietly, " I have been looking for thee."

" Peter," said she, very very quietly, " and I have been waiting for thee."

And because most of the people had begun to hurry away out of the gathering storm, and few any longer were about, he gave her a brave kiss did Peter, and told her she was the jewel of his world and tooked her back to her mother.

It was from that mortal night my Faither and my Mother rode alongside each other on the wagon-star of luck, as you might say, for Peter was he and Rosie was she, and how could they be anybody else?

Their world turned out always as happy as that night had been, bless the sleeping hearts of 'em. . . . First at his shepherd's work under Rushup Edge it was, and then, when he had tooked up farming in a smallish way that grew biggish and prospered more and more as time went on, here at Red Oak.

It was a queer start, being tokened like that, I do admit, but it showed vast credit on the scientific man for sartain-sure.

The scientific man he told your Faither's faither, after parson had done his share, that he was going to tell about it to the big folk and swell folk he knowed in London. Wonderful it seemed to the few hereabouts who larnt the secret after he had gone away, though he had but said it was simply a basket full of mean and paltry hearts and little souls and imitations, with naught but one among them made of proper metal. And down among those mean and paltry imitations, he would say, comed the magic ring, and ferreted there to find the heart that was truest and sweetest and bestest, the pick of the basket.

And he told my Mother, when Faither weren't about, that sterling metal shall always find its like.

Hector Bolitho

MR. AND MRS. PERRY

WHEN Jim Perry married he took his wife to live in the little house tucked in behind the blacksmith's shop. It had been no more than a tumble-down shack, the victim of wind and rain, when they went to see it in the first summer of their betrothal, but their shy ecstasy had made the uncertain stairs, the chinks and the split floor boards all part of the beauty they had found together. They were in love and this house was to be their home. Jim was not the handiest man in the village for nothing. While Jill dug up the little square yard, planting the six hollyhocks the postmistress had given her, the line of daffodils and the primroses she had filched from the woods, Jim built a new staircase. He patched the structure and papered the bedrooms so that even his harsh mother-in-law admitted that it was all so spick and span you could have eaten your dinner off the kitchen floor.

From the first day when they stood alone in the little bed-room, with the sprigs of gentians on the wallpaper, Jill and Jim were perfectly happy. Nobody could ever say that their life was like a novel because it began and ended without anxiety or surprise. Their house was shielded from the street by the blacksmith's shop so they felt that their life together was something apart from the jealousy and bickering of the village. The only noises they ever heard were from Jim's own saw in the workshop downstairs and the clang of the blacksmith's hammer on the anvil. " Just like as if our wedding bells was ringing every day in the year," Jill once said. The memory of her little joke was stirred every time they heard the hammer strike the anvil. It was a bond between them, for ever at hand. Leaning over the stove, dipping her plump hands into the soap-suds or polishing the gay copper bed-warmer which was all that Jill had inherited in the way of possessions, she would listen to the blacksmith's hammer and know that downstairs Jim was listening too. No, nobody could say their life was as good as a novel for it ran like a rill, for ever in the sunshine, with neither shadow nor flood to give excitement to its journey.

Almost every broken chair and table in Thimble Stanton was brought to Jim's workshop to be repaired. He made the pedestal for the inn-keeper's wife so that her aspidistra would be high and out of the way of noisy customers who had a habit of emptying their beer dregs into it. He built a porch on to the chapel and he made a new bottom for the old wood-box at Thornton Hall. It was this last job that directed Jim Perry's thoughts along a new way. The wood-box was a fine old Tudor coffer, decorated on three sides with linen-fold panelling and made of oak so old that it was as hard as iron. " Rather nice old things, aren't they? " Jim said, as he wrapped a piece of sacking about the coffer before it went back to the Hall. In the months that followed, as he worked upon a deal table for the school-room, an oak settle for the rector's golden-wedding present, and the dull little mending jobs which fell to him, he often thought of the old oak coffer. He ever found that while he lay half asleep in the early morning his eye would follow the line of the carving and his hands would seem to remember the pleasure of touching the beautiful dark wood.

If there was one day of faint excitement in the lives of Jill and Jim Perry it was on the second anniversary of their wedding. Jill came down stairs in the morning to find a vast obstacle in her way, covered with newspapers.

" Well I never, Jim, what is this? " she asked.

He whisked the newspaper sheets from the coffer with a brisk flourish. " It's for you, Jill, for to-day. I made it myself when you wasn't looking. It's old, Jill, the oak is. It's made of real old oak, like the one at the Hall every bit of it. Panels an' all. I carved it myself with my own hands."

Jill knelt down and stroked the coffer. " Made it for me. Made it yourself, Jim? " she asked. " Oh, you are fibbin'. It's wonderful. Did you really make it yourself? "

" Of course I did, all by myself. "

She stood up and ran her fingers along the edge of the lid. Then she stretched her hand out to him, almost faint from the glory of what she knew; that she was loved. Then she fell into his arms and cried like a child. God Himself seemed to have walked into the little house that day. They left the coffer in its ridiculous place right in front of the door. They moved about it and stared. It was not until late in the evening that Jill said, " We must take it upstairs, Jim; we can't leave it here, can we? " They carried the coffer to their bedroom and Jill lifted the lid. She placed her wedding dress, her fair straw hat and her six handkerchiefs in it, and then Jill and Jim crept into their bed and slept.

The secret of the coffer was not theirs for very long. Jill's mother told the postmistress and the postmistress, a tireless gossip, soon told all Thimble Stanton. Sir George Thornton himself came and climbed the stairs to see the wonder. " I couldn't tell it from the original," he said. " Perry, you are a real craftsman, and a wily one too, for it's a fine piece of work."

It was thus that Jim came to carve the pulpit for the new church at Handsworth and the panelling for Thornton Hall. When a year had passed the villagers no longer dared bring their crippled chairs to Jim's workshop. He still lived in the little house and he was still awakened each morning by the clang of the blacksmith's hammer. But, fifty yards along the High Street, his new shop was furnished with fine old glass and Queen Anne chests of drawers; tall clocks and walnut dining-room chairs. The sign ANTIQUES hung over the door and Jim became known as the most skilled restorer of old furniture in all his part of Essex.

C

George Whitehead was twenty-five when he came to work for Jim Perry. "It'll be rather nice to have a man your own age," Jill said. "You don't want an old fogey about the place, do you? And it'll be someone to talk to." For three days they had worried over the problem. "I can't do all this extra panelling myself, can I?" he had said.

And Jill had frowned at first and asked, "But wouldn't it be nice to keep it like it is, small, to ourselves?"

Then she had reproached herself for her selfishness. He seemed such a child in some ways. With his tools in his hands and a fine piece of wood to work on, some magic knowledge came to his fingers. But he was an awkward and forgetful man at all else and Jill supplied these needs in him with the watchfulness of a mother. She did not realize why, when he was tired, she held him against her heart as if he were a little boy, more in need of her than she was in need of him.

Jill changed her voice when she realized that she had been thinking only of herself. She laughed a little as she said, "Of course, what duffers women are! Of course have George Whitehead to work with you. You couldn't do all that panelling yourself. But you will do the finishing, won't you, because it will be a sort of piece of history for you to have done all of a fine room like that at the Hall. Your life work you might call it."

Jim smiled. He liked her to treat him as something of an artist. It was strange that with her ignorance of his work she knew by instinct what he felt and what his tools meant to him. She had reverence for things she did not understand. That was the quality in her which Jim loved, although he could not have defined it in those words. "It's your hands, Jim," she said to him once. "You've got artistic hands. That's what it is. Mine is just working hands. But yours are delicate and your fingers is long. That's the artist's hands."

Sometimes she watched his hands when he was asleep and she would tremble when he touched her; when he turned sometimes to draw her to him, gentle and shy as a boy. He

would whisper, " I love you, Jill," and she would answer, " I
love you, too, Jim," and the fresh exchange of the old declaration would soothe her and give a new benediction to her sleep.

" You'd better ask George Whitehead to come and take a
cup of tea," she said. " It'll make it more friendly like. You
wouldn't treat him as if he was only workin' for you. You
know what I mean. It'd seem nicer if he came and had a cup
of tea and talked it over."

George Whitehead came to tea on Saturday when the shop
was closed. He wore his dark blue serge suit and held his
bowler hat as if it burned his fingers.

Jill took his hat from him as he sat down. " And will you
take sugar, one spoon or two, Mr. Whitehead? " she asked.

" One'll do nicely, thank you Mrs. Perry," he answered.

Jim Perry was shy and silent. Jill and Mr. Whitehead talked
of the garden. " Aye, it's horseradish and nettles what's the
gardener's worst friends, don't you think, Mr. Whitehead? "
said Jill. " Why, even in our bit of a garden you can dig down
until your back breaks, gettin' at those horseradish roots. But
they come up again, before you can turn round, as you might
say."

" Well, my mother used to say she just didn't understand
why the Almighty made nettles," said Mr. Whitehead. The
talk went on, but they did not seem able to broach the
subject of whether George Whitehead would come to work
in the shop.

" But it's worth while, the work you put into it," said Jill.
" I like to see the flowers. A bit of colour."

" Brightens things up, doesn't it? " said George Whitehead.

Jill smiled at Jim. " Mr. Perry doesn't like bright colours, do
you Jim? " she said. " He likes quiet colours, like mahogany
browns and that sort. He's got an old pipe—what is it called,
Jim? "

" It's a meerschaum," he said.

" He just loves that pipe, don't you, you can't deny it. You know, Mr. Whitehead, he'll hold it up and say, ' Now that's a pretty colour, all mottled like that ' as if it was, well, you know."

" Well, there's nothing like the colour of a good piece of walnut to me," answered George Whitehead.

At last Jill felt that they were near the question of which they were all so shy. " Mr. Perry will be with you there, Mr. Whitehead," she said. " He's crazy about old wood." Then she added, nervously, " It'll be nice if you can come and work with Mr. Perry, Mr. Whitehead."

Jim looked towards her and smiled gratefully.

" Oh, I can all right, Mrs. Perry. And nothing would suit me better, it being my own village and all that."

So George Whitehead came to work in the antique shop. A corner was cleared for him and a great bench built beneath a window. The pungent stink of his glue pot and the whine of his saw were added to the smells and sounds of the shop and, working together, Jim and his assistant carved the nine hundred and twenty linen-fold panels for the new room at Thornton Hall. Every afternoon at four o'clock Jill would set out with a jug of hot tea, bread and butter and three slices of cake. George Whitehead would wash his hands beneath the tap in the yard, but not until Jim had done so, then all three would sit about a table on which Jill spread a blue and white check cloth.

As the years passed the shop became more full of odds and ends. Broken Windsor chairs were tied to the rafters, pieces of panelling and empty picture frames were piled in the corners. For the first few years Jill would pounce on the conglomeration now and then and say, " I am going to have a good tidy up." But the muddle became too much for her and the shop was left to its pleasant confusion. A film of dust and a friendly network of cobwebs settled in the dark corners but the pieces of furniture in the window were always spick and span, with their prices on small tickets, hidden in discreet places.

George Whitehead and Jim Perry never learned to speak to each other more than was necessary. The foundation of their trust grew, but they remained shy and never fell into the familiarity of Christian names. The stiffness of their first meeting over the tea cups never wholly faded from their talk. George Whitehead dined with Jill and Jim every Easter and Christmas. Even then, with port and cigars to temper their reserve, they talked only of their work, life in the village, or the prospects of spring in the garden. Jill would say, " Do you remember the year when the hollyhocks were as high as the lintel," and Jim would plead, " Now, Mr. Whitehead, do have another cigar." " Yes, do," Jill would add, " I like the smell of cigars, don't I, Jim? " And Jim would reply, " Yes, and do you know, she makes me smoke one every evening. It's extravagant habits, don't you think, for the likes of us? "

Then a slow smile would warm George Whitehead's face as he answered, " Oh well, Mr. Perry, we're getting on, and if we can't have a bit of pleasure what's the use of living, you might say."

Only once Jill broke the delicate fabric of their established shyness. It was Christmas and George Whitehead had said, towards the end of the evening, " Well, I'd better be on my way. One must get to bed some time." It was then that Jill answered, " Well, it's time you had a wife and settled down like me and Mr. Perry."

They were silent then, as if they had touched a truth better left alone. George Whitehead took his hat from the hall, and his coat, and he barely thanked them as he hurried into the December cold. Jill had touched the old but unhealed wound of his loneliness. He had thought of marriage, many times, but he was forty now, and his habits were set. He went back to his lodgings next to the Rose and Crown and lay awake a long time, too troubled to sleep.

*   *   *

A shiver of alarm went through the village when the new barmaid came to the Rose and Crown, with her bleached hair, blister pearl ear-rings and a cage with two budgerigars. When she went to the post office on the first day and asked, " Any letters for Miss Bat," the postmistress put the opinion of the village in a nutshell when she said, " That sort cannot last in Thimble Stanton."

Flossie Bat had been in the village only three weeks when the spirit lamp with which she heated her curling tongs over-turned and set the Rose and Crown on fire. It was half past eleven in the evening, before her day off, when the villagers turned out of their beds to watch the flames and to see Flossie Bat running up and down, her hair streaming behind her and her shrill voice crying, " Oh me budgerigars. And, oh, me fur coat." The flames burned the old inn as if it were made of matchwood and then they spread on, devouring three cottages on the way. The cottage in which George Whitehead lived was burned to the ground. He stood before the roaring fury in his grey flannel pyjamas, holding his mother's chiming clock in one hand and a bundle of clothes in the other.

Only the babies and the very old stayed in their beds that night. Seven hundred of the eight hundred and forty people in Thimble Stanton stared at the spectacle of leaping flames and falling timbers. Jim Perry made his way through the crowd and found George Whitehead, a pathetic figure in his pyjamas, whispering, " I've lost my all. I've lost my all." Jim took his arm with one hand, and, holding the clock in the other, he made a way through the mass of silent, gaping people.

Jim became less shy at the sight of the poor man's distress. " Now, come right along with me. Don't take on so. No, you mustn't. Mrs. Perry is making up the spare bedroom for you. She said you mustn't be cut up about it."

George Whitehead was too dazed to be cut up. It was not until he stood in the Perry's sitting-room that he became conscious of his strange appearance. He realized that Jill Perry was looking at him while he was wearing no more than his grey flannel pyjamas.

"I'm that ashamed, you seeing me like this, Mrs. Perry," he said.

Jill was magnificent in the crisis. "Oh, don't think about *that*, Mr. Whitehead. In a time like this those things don't matter, do they? We are all put on this earth to do what we can for one another."

George Whitehead climbed the stairs and Jim and Jill showed him into the spare bedroom. A pair of Jim's pyjamas were hung over the end of the bed, with a towel, and a candle burned on the table.

"Now don't trouble yourself about a thing," Jim said. "You can stay here until you can find a place. And you can buy what you need in the morning. There won't be any business done to-morrow in Thimble Stanton, you can bet. And it's market day in Braintree so you can go over in the early 'bus."

Jill said, "Good-night, Mr. Whitehead," through the doorway and when she had gone to their room Jim followed her. As they lay in the darkness, their hands held one in the other beneath the clothes, Jill said, "We must be awful kind to him now, mustn't we, Jim?"

He held her hand more tightly. "Yes, dear, of course we must. And we must spare him a few pounds to help him a bit. He's a good sort and I couldn't get along without him."

Jill was silent. She thought of the man in the next room not as George Whitehead, but just as a man who was alone in the world and in need of help. She lifted Jim's arm and placing her cheek in his hand she went to sleep.

Next morning, George Whitehead caught the early bus to Braintree and came back with a new suit of clothes and a parcel of shirts and socks. Jill took the price labels off them and folded them into a drawer of the dressing table in the spare room.

The village was crazy with excitement during the days

following the fire. The drab rival of the Rose and Crown, at
the far end of the village, did a roaring trade in beer and gossip.
But the drama passed, and when he had been staying with the
Perrys for a week, George Whitehead said that he would look
out for a room somewhere in the village when he finished his
work in the shop that evening.

"For that matter you could take the day off," Jim said.
"But what's the hurry? The spare room is there and nobody
using it. Let it wait for a day or two." Jim looked anxiously
at Jill, lest she did not agree. But she smiled her encourage-
ment and said, "Of course, Mr. Whitehead, stay as long as
you please. The room's doing nothing as Mr. Perry says.
There's no need to be fussing yourself yet."

And so the days passed. The blackened beams were cleared
from the scene of the fire and the foundations of a new inn
were dug into the charred earth. George Whitehead stayed on
with the Perrys in their house behind the blacksmith's shop
and as time went on Jill and Jim no longer spoke of "the spare
room". They called it, "Mr. Whitehead's room". The final
sign that their home was also his came when he carried his
mother's chiming clock downstairs on Sunday morning and
said, "Would you mind having it down here where we can
all see the time? It's a good time-keeper. My mother was left
it by her mother before her."

"Now that's very nice of you, Mr. Whitehead," said Jill.
"We can stand it on the mantel where we can all see the time.
It'll keep us up to the mark."

The clock, which had already governed the coming and going
of two generations, ticked out the hours of the three calm lives.
Jill and Jim and George Whitehead grew old together, like
three trees enjoying the same expanse of earth, yet each in his
and her own way. Jim Perry seemed to wither with time. He
became little and bent but although his feet shuffled and his
voice became slow and croaky, his hands never lost their talent.
They still chiselled patterns from old oak and made cabinets

with drawers that ran as smooth as silk. Jill worked in her garden. She became fat when she was in her fifties. She liked to put on her black dress in the afternoon to walk to the shop, with the sedateness of age, carrying the jug of tea, the bread and butter and slices of cake. As she grew old she became sentimentally kind about all the world. No miscreant came into their talk without her finding some excuse for his weakness and whenever gossip crept in past the blacksmith's shop, to her doorstep, she deftly turned it away. Even when the flamboyant Flossie Bat was recalled, Jill sighed and said, " Well, she must have had some good in her because she liked birds. That sort's always lonely." The essence of her marriage to Jim was that neither of them had ever known what it was to be alone.

George Whitehead kept his strength to the end of his life, and as Jim Perry became quite old and less able to lift the heavy furniture, the stronger man did all the heavy work in the shop. He had been living with the Perrys twenty years when Jim died. All the morning he had felt that he could barely move about the shop. He had watched his weakening energies in alarm; as he might have watched a clock, croaking its last chime. When he went home for his midday meal he said, " You know, Jill, I'm feeling a bit queer and I think I'll take it easy this afternoon."

George Whitehead went back to the shop and left them alone. They sat at the table for a long time in silence. Jill watched her husband. He was pale and his hands moved slowly. He looked up and saw her anxious eyes.

" What's troubling you, Jill? " he asked.

" You're not yourself, Jim, I can see. I think I'll fetch a doctor."

" No, no," he protested. " Don't fuss about nothing. I'm just a bit tired, that's all."

He stood up from the table and walked towards his chair by the fire. George Whitehead's clock chimed three. " A nice chime that, Jill," Jim said. " Working with old clocks teaches you to understand them. There's a deal of silver in that bell."

She rose and walked near him. Outside they could hear the blacksmith's hammer, joyously ringing on the anvil. "Can you hear it, Jim," she said. "They've never stopped ringing, have they, our marriage bells." He smiled and kissed her. Then he crumpled and fell against her. She held him for a moment. The last muscle in his body relaxed and she lifted him forward into the chair.

*   *   *

When a year had passed Jill Perry and George Whitehead were married quietly in the rector's study. After Jim had died George Whitehead had gone to live in a room in the new inn and Jill had taken over the management of the shop. But this was not her province. She looked askance when a woman asked her if she had any Battersea enamel candlesticks. A chest of drawers was no more than a chest of drawers to her, although she knew that the drawers should run smoothly because Jim had always made them that way. She trembled with anxiety whenever George Whitehead left the shop because somebody might come in with a piece of furniture to sell. Time and again she had to run over to the inn and beg him to come back. "I don't know what I'd do without you, Mr. White-head," she would say when the customer had gone.

For a year Jill struggled in her loneliness. One evening George Whitehead paused by the door of the shop and turned back. Jill looked down as he asked her to marry him. "It'd make it easier, maybe, Mrs. Perry," he said. Then, with terrible courage which made his blood thump in his heart, he said, "It isn't as if I was a young man. It's because you and Mr. Perry was always so kind to me that I'd like to help you. It would be different, with us, you see." Jill still looked down as he said, "Love-making is over for the likes of me, Mrs. Perry, and all I want is to be there in the house to protect you, and look after the shop."

Jill thought of none but Jim all the morning of her wedding day. She knew that if he had been able to speak—if there had been a brief moment of consciousness before he died —he would have told her to do this. She went back over the whispered talks they had had as they lay in bed. In her heart she knew that she was not breaking faith with him now.

George Whitehead came for her and they walked to the rectory together in the afternoon. The kind old rector had known them both since they were children and he had married Jill to Jim Perry. He gave them the benison they needed as he said, " I think you are both doing what is right. It is good that the young should love, but it is also a fine and noble thing, when the troubles of our existence are almost ended, that two old people should come together in the autumn of their lives and live as friends. There is one who is in our memories now, who looks down upon you from his heavenly throne, and I am sure there is a smile of happiness and contentment upon his face."

Thus soothed, they went back to the house and when evening fell they sat at the table where they had sat so often with Jim, in the old days. It was Jill who broke the silence. She became quite gay as she swept away the gravity that had settled on them. She alone knew why. She alone heard the blacksmith's hammer ringing on the anvil.

" It's just like old times, isn't it? " she said. " Jim would like to see us having our supper together, I'm sure."

When their meal was ended they washed the dishes. Then they moved towards the fire. George Whitehead sat in the chair he had always used, but Jill bade him move to Jim's chair, nearer to the fire. Then she went to the cupboard and brought out a box of cigars. " I hope they aren't stale," she said. " They was the last ones Jim ever bought in Braintree."

George Whitehead took a cigar and as he smoked it, Jill inhaled the familiar smell. The clock chimed ten and Jill thought of Jim's remark, " There's a deal of silver in that bell."

George Whitehead threw the stump of his cigar in the fire and Jill rose from her chair. It was strange how easily she fell back into her old habits. She emptied the ash tray into the grate and then she lifted the fireguard into its place.

" I suppose it's time we went to bed, don't you think so? " she said.

They lighted their candles and climbed the stairs. Jill walked towards her bedroom door and George Whitehead towards his. He paused, as he had always paused before, and said, " Good-night, Mrs. Perry."

Jill answered, " Good-night, Mr. Whitehead." Then they closed the doors of their rooms and the little house went to sleep.

H. E. Bates

TIME-EXPIRED

MISS BURKE, who was Irish and at pains to explain that she did not like men, stood on the open airstrip watching the wounded being loaded into the dusty Dakota. Her sun-burned face had the deep Irish upperlip; she had square shoulders and in her khaki drill she did not look like a nurse. She looked rather like a man who has indecisively begun to let his hair grow long and then has become slightly self-conscious of it and tucked it under his cap. When the wind that churned the soft yellow dust of the airstrip into high smoky clouds came beating under the body of the Dakota it caught the edges of Miss Burke's masculine short back hairs and blew into them sudden small dimples, as into the fur of a cat. The dust had everywhere the fineness of powdered sulphur. It settled like fine sprayed paint on the dark wings of the plane, on the fabric of the ambulance, and even on the bear-brown blanket of the stretchers, whenever for a moment or two a wounded man was set down. Whenever a plane took off or landed out in the runway, dust rose up into the clear air with oppressive insistence in huge yellow smoky columns, and clashed then against the harder, yellower light of sun. It seemed to make even more oppressive the oppressive heat of the shadeless afternoon. Only Miss Burke was not oppressed by it. Miss Burke, who had been nearly three years a nurse on the Burma battlefield, was quite used to most things now.

In about another five minutes all the stretchers were in the body of the plane, strung from the roof traces and ready for take-off, and the crew were pushing past them into the nose.

The men on the stretchers did not seem to Miss Burke any different from the men on the stretchers of any other day. They were a series of rigid and nameless bodies covered by brown blankets : a couple of Indian boys, turned Chinese yellow by pain and shock, and the rest British boys, pale too and rather impassive, staring stiffly upward at the dark green roof of the fuselage. For some reason mostly leg wounds to-day, so that the men, set in plaster, had something of the look of bits of broken statuary. Nobody acutely bad. Nobody screaming anyway.

Miss Burke got into the plane and sat down on the edge of the iron seat opposite the door. One of the ground boys came almost directly afterwards and shut the door, and in that moment all the dazzling dustiness of the afternoon was shut away. Miss Burke sat with her hands in her pockets, listening to first one and then the other of the engines being started, until both were roaring together. Then as the plane began slowly to move out, away from dispersal tents, to the open runway, she glanced impersonally up at the wounded, sus-pended like a double row of carcasses in oblong hammocks. They were all quite quiet.

As the plane turned into the runway and then began to move down it, in a moment or two very fast, Miss Burke hung on to the nearest strap. There were no belts in the Dakota, but she liked to hang on to the strap, just in case. The runway seemed to bump a little and it did not occur to her, until she suddenly looked up, that there might be, for men on those slightly swaying stretchers, a feeling of insecurity. Even then she did not move. If anything happened you were all helpless anyway.

It was only when she saw an arm being slowly lifted up and down from the foremost stretcher that she realized something was wrong. The signal annoyed her a little. No sooner air-borne than somebody, she thought, starts binding. They were hardly even airborne. That was men, if you like, all over. The plane lifted itself off the earth exactly at the moment that her own impatience lifted her mind, and in the same way: in a slow unsurprising pull, as of something so often repeated that it had ceased to astonish her.

She walked up the body of the plane, levelled out now, to where the hand was waving limply to beckon her. It was one of the leg cases: an English boy with his left leg entirely encased, like a piece of masonry. His face had once been very brown, but now it had turned, under shock, to the very lustreless colour of the dust they had left behind. She saw at once, by trained instinct, that he was very tired.

" Something wrong? " She had trained herself to speak not loudly but visually, with exaggerated movement of her big Irish lips, so that now, at once, the boy was sure what she said. She had trained herself also to record answers, and those also visually, so as not to strain against the noise of the plane.

" Are we up? " the boy said.

For crying out loud, Miss Burke thought, where in the name of God does he think we are? Only a man would ask it. She looked out of the window. They had climbed to four or five hundred feet, and down below, already, the tents of the airfield had begun to look like sun-baked sea-shells on a sandy lake between stunted fringes of palms. Beyond this, in all directions, the low jungle was assuming its dark wavy relief, spreading outward in huge monotonous sections unbroken except by the sulphury vein of tiny roads.

She turned her head and nodded. She did not know if there was anything she could say. Idiotic to ask him if by any chance he thought they weren't going to get up. Idiotic to discuss remote chances against the roar of two engines. She swallowed hard, and the noise of the engines changed its note. Idiotic to talk to him anyway.

" How long shall we be? " the boy said.

" I wouldn't be knowin'," Miss Burke said, " we'll get there when we'll get there."

" Where are we going? "

" I wouldn't be knowin' that either," she said. " Maybe we're taking you to Comilla. Maybe we're not."

He moved restlessly, troubled, turned his head towards her and then, seeing the window, turning it abruptly back again. She knew then that he was afraid of looking out of the plane; she knew that he had never flown before. Of course that was idiotic too, and she wasn't going to have any unprofessional nonsense about it.

" All you have to do is shut your eyes and get some sleep," she said. " The other boys are asleep. Now come along."

" I can't," the boy said. As he shook his head she saw how deeply the eyes had receded through shock and exhaustion and pure pain.

" What do you mean you can't!" she said. " Of course you can. If you can't sleep you can shut your eyes."

" That's what I can't do," the boy said. " I can't shut them. They won't shut. They won't stay shut."

She swallowed hard and did not answer. Really it was very exhausting talking like this against the noise of engines; it couldn't go on. She looked down with severity at the agitated face, with its dark eyes so sharply impelled by shock that they had become frozenly transfixed, but for some reason or other she did not know what to say. And while she was trying to make up her mind the boy began talking again, this time not exactly to her, not in continuance of anything that had been said before, but simply in pure aimless relief and excitement. She had sense enough to let him go on. And after a moment or two, hearing all the time less than half he said, she sat down in the seat again and rested her head back against the metal of the fuselage, in a pretence of listening. She realised then that all he needed was an object of reception for the things he had to say, and that its identity did not matter much, nor what it said in answer. And so she let him go on, while the plane flew steadily on its level course at about four thousand feet, over the green encrusted contours of jungle and palm-fenced strips of water glittering in the white heat of afternoon.

For the next half hour she caught at intervals some intelligible phrase in the jumble of things he had to say, and now and then she would nod automatically in reply, as if to indicate that she was still listening. She was not so much bored as very sleepy herself. She expected him at any moment to talk about his mother. For God's sake, she thought, they're just like babies. The more you sympathize with them the more you may. She was determined not to hear any nonsense like that; she never did. But twice in quick succession the aircraft suddenly gave a violent bump in the heat. It was nothing serious, but it threw her about the seat with a jerk, and she saw the boy's hand flung out as if to save himself from falling. She stretched up and caught it and held it in hers. The palm was clammy with sweat.

" We'll be all right when we're over the sea," she said. " It's just the heat. That's all."

He turned to her and gave her a slow and possibly apathetic smile. For God's sake, she thought, I hope he's not going to be sick. Not that I ought to pander to any of this emotional nonsense at all. What in the name o' God would Johnson say if she could see me? Johnson was a sister up at Comilla. They shared a tent and called each other Johnson and Burke, as if Christian names were a soft concession not to be tolerated. In three years they had watched a constant stream of mutilated men come down from the front, in heat and in rain, at all times of the year, from every quarter from Imphal down to Akyab and Mandalay. It was one of her ambitions to see Mandalay.

" Did you come down from Mandalay? " she said to the boy.

" That's where I got it," he said, and pointed to the leg.

" Ah," she said.

" Two days ago." His face was restless with fresh anxiety, the lids of the eyes stiffly held open. And then suddenly he came to the point of it all; he made a sudden wild grab as it

D

were at the hot core of his own personal catastrophe : the thing that had been troubling him all the time. " I was time-expired," he said. " Time-expired. Three more days and I'd have had this bloody country. This lousy stinking bloody country." He grew for a moment or two pathetically excited. " I'd have had it. I was going home."

Weak and immobile, his eyes held in them the smallest of solitary tears, so that even Miss Burke was for a moment or two touched by them in spite of herself. Now she knew why he could not shut his eyes. She did not know what to say, and suddenly the boy was silent too. She waited for some moments for him to speak again, but he was still quiet and at last she said, " Well, you'll be going home now. It's all the same. You'll be going home anyway."

He did not answer even that. Now that at last he had been able to disclose the pain that really bothered him it was as if it had never existed. It was not the wound but the circumstances that seemed to be destroyed by the wound that troubled him. He seemed quite at rest because of Miss Burke's understanding.

Miss Burke looked out of the small round window of the plane. Below, the jungle was breaking up, and rivers in which she could see shadows of pale brown sand like muscles under the transparent blue skin of water were beginning to appear and broaden among the mass of trees. She knew that they were coming to the sea.

She sat thinking about the boy being time-expired. Yes : she understood that. There was no one in the whole country who would not understand it. To be going home, to be at the end of exile : for God's sake who didn't know? One day she would be time-expired too. It was only at the rarest moments that she could think of it. But one day it would happen. She would be time-expired and there would be an end for her of the heat and sweat and the dust of summer and the miserable steaming nights of the monsoon, and the callous clash of death

in every part of her life. There would be an end of the grey
vultures feeding on the dead. They said time went quickly
in the East, and that after a while you could not separate the
memory of one individual day from another. But what
happened really was that time built itself up into a mass of
hard white light behind you, like an impersonal and glittering
wall that cut you off from the shadowy remembrances of all
your life behind it. That was what she hated; she knew that
that was what the soldier hated, what they all hated. To be
time-expired meant that you were going to break down that
wall, break through it, break out into the resurrected memory
of a sort of life that mattered. She had worked through the
heat of the plains for three steaming summers without trying
to think of it too much. They used to say that it was not the
climate for white women—no, it was certainly not the climate.
Nor was war exactly their destiny either. But there you are:
in time you took the heat and the dust and the war and the
blood and all the lunatic filth of India because there was nothing else you could do. You were caught in a violent trap. You
had to stay. And your only hope of escape from it was that
somewhere, some time, if you were lucky and if you could
outlive the heat and the cancer of your unshed tears you would
become, at last, time-expired. You would be going home.

She looked down out of the window and there now, breaking
in a series of glistening lines of white contour that seemed
transfixed against the strip of yellow sand, was the sea. Did
anyone at home, she thought, understand what it meant? There
were times when she thought that the whole front—all of
them, the men, the pilots, the nurses—had been forgotten.
They had sometimes said it themselves: a forgotten army of
forgotten men. They had been overshadowed—oh! yes, she
knew that, but the shadow of it did not darken the heat or
diminish the glassy impact of their time in exile.

For God's sake there was no use thinking about it. "We are
over the sea now," she said to the boy. "Going up the coast."

He smiled. " First time I've flown," he said.

And God knows, she thought, you're a lucky man to be able to fly. Do you know where you'd be if it weren't for the Daks, coming to fetch you out? You'd be time-expired all right. You'd be rotting forgotten somewhere up in that God-forsaken jungle because there'd be no way of getting you out. You, and the Lord knew how many more—you'd have just died up there, wherever you lay. You should all of you go down, she thought, on your bended knees, and thank the stars of heaven there were enough Daks to feed and water and supply you and then when you were wounded bring you out again.

She rested her head against the fuselage and shut her eyes for the first time. Her ears had become slightly blocked by the noise of engines and she had forgotten to swallow and it was quite quiet in her head. Shut away into her own world, she gave herself up to a momentary contemplation of things that were not real. She began to allow herself to think that she too was going home. There were no longer any blistering dusty airstrips, no longer any hordes of vultures pouring like bloated grey beetles over the carcasses of the dead, no longer any savage steaming days when you hated the sun. There was no longer any exile, no longer any of that arid female life in transit camps, or of a life with men who, because they were fighting or tired or occupied elsewhere, did not want you. There was an end of all the callous futility of war. She was going home to a place where the rain fell deeply and quietly on green grass, not with the madness of the monsoon, and where the pure light and penetration of it would wash the dust forever out of her bones.

She held on to these thoughts for the remaining half hour of the flight. The wounded all about her were very quiet. The boy made no attempt to speak to her until the aircraft, banking, began to make its circuit of the field. Even then she did not open her eyes but clung on a little longer to an inner world remote from everything she knew to be real. She even shut her eyes a little tighter and held her hands painfully on the edges of the metal seat, and thought " God, how much longer? How much longer? How much, much longer? "

And then her eyes were open. She made them open with brutal suddenness. She stood up on her feet and saw that the boy's stretcher was swaying slightly as the aircraft turned. She held it still again, with instinctive efficiency.

" Coming in to land," she said, and stood looking down at him. Once again he smiled, and once again she was aware of his helplessness : that same childish masculine helplessness that was always drawing forth her contempt. But she was not contemptuous now.

" Where's your home? " she said.

" Shropshire," he said.

" Nice there? "

He nodded and smiled but did not speak. She saw the small glint of tears in his eyes again and thought : " For God's sake, any moment now and he'll be asking me for my address."

And I am not, she thought, having any of that.

She turned away and looked out of the window and saw the landscape below coming to life : palms beyond the black runway, bright fronds of banana trees drooping in the heat, a mass of crimson bougainvillea flaming by a long cane basha, some coolies running. And in a few moments it was all flattening out and seeming suddenly to take on its own speed, and presently she knew by the bump of the wheels that they were down.

As the Dakota taxied to dispersal she turned for the last time to look at the boy. He was relieved and glad that the flight was over. It would be a long time before he was well but before long, if he were lucky, he would be going home. He at least was really time-expired.

" Shropshire for you," she said, and then walked briskly back through the aircraft just as the pilot cut the engines. There was no sense waiting for an answer.

She stood by the big double doors of the Dakota and in a

moment or two, when they were opened, the heat and glare of the afternoon rushed in and oppressingly dazzled her face. She helped get the steps out herself, and was the first person to go down them.

She jumped down on the hot sandy concrete and looked about her. For God's sake, nothing but men. All helpless as usual. All standing about and gaping as if they'd never seen a man on a stretcher before. Two clots of Indian drivers were propping up the two ambulances and two British boys, bare to the waist and brown as burnt butter, were not much better.

"Come on, come on," Miss Burke said. "Come on!"

She stood in the fierce sunlight waiting for the stretchers to come out of the plane. To her they came out as they had gone in : a series of anonymous oblongs, plaster-encased, like lumps of nameless statuary. She did not even know which of them differed from another. And when the boy from Shropshire was brought out, last but one, eyes fixed upon her as if either searching for a sign of friendliness or as if she were something very wonderful, she did not even glance at him in return.

Instead she walked deliberately away from the plane to where, by the ambulances, there was some confusion now. The clots couldn't count the ambulance capacity and were trying to get in more men than the vehicles would hold. For the love of God, for God's sake, she thought, just like men. Just like men! As helpless as babies. Just like men.

"Can't you count now?" she said, raising her voice. "It's the bunch of wet-heads you are, isn't it? You clots, you dead-beats! Can't you see there's a man lying in the sun? Is it round the damn bend all of you are? Get that man out of the sun!"

She marched about among the men and the waiting stretchers with an intense impatience, her voice hard and strong and her eyes impersonal at last again in the deadly glare of light.

"Do you think we've got the whole of life to spend here?" she said. "Do you think we've nothing else to do?"

V. Sackville-West

ADVENTURING

YOU happy baby at the cottage door,
  Finding your legs, adventuring on life,
Run; stagger; topple; cut your knees on pebbles;
Howl for your mother; sob within her arms.

Comfort at hand, for that small injury,
That tiny smear of blood, that simple kiss.
Your mother wears her household apron, goes
About her ploys, but picks you up for this.

Where is your father? ah, who knows, who knows?
Perhaps on tilted stretcher travelling
Down difficult mountain at this very hour,
You scrap of innocence, you ignorant flower.

Only your mother busy, silent, numb,
Senses within her blood-stream what he bears;
He who is part of her, her cherished one,
The sharer of most secret secrets; dumb.

One night he loved your mother, and you live;
Your sturdy knees, now grazed, were made that night;
So was your heart you know not of, not yet;
All these were made, and have long ways to travel.

Run; chase the kitten; stumble on the gravel;
Cut, cut yourself, and learn the little pain.
Pain you will have enough, pain worse and bitter,
My innocent, before you reach the end.

SARK GIRL

Guy Malet

H. M. Tomlinson

THE LITTLE THINGS

THE frost held. Winter had settled on us. It rested as hard, as cold, and as unrelenting as the midnight broadcast. What could be done about either? Nothing, except bend in supplication to Providence. It is too late now to think of trying to compass the least matter for oneself; as well as we know anything, the Secretary for Air ordains our weather, as somebody else governs our potatoes. The frost was still and deep. To remember a sunny bank of thyme in a south wind, and all's well, was no better than that foolish dream we have now and then of peace, and the sky as silent as it used to be when we were children, with only slow white clouds there, in the days before men were so clever.

So yesterday morning I was out on some errand, perhaps to learn, if I could, in the winter of which year the coals might come, or perhaps humbly to petition the junta of local office-holders to allow our windows to be replaced again, as arctic draughts eddying round a room where one must be can distract attention from the eternal truth itself. I was out on this errand, whatever it was, perhaps only to post a letter, and noted without relief or any other emotion that the local signal was at All Clear (which might have been a lie, for boys lark about with that sign, and good luck to them), and was frowning over the latest piece of world news. Now, what did that mean?

In fact, I walked in two fogs. The perceptible one was white, thin and icy, and the trees in it were ghostly. The snow deadened all sound except where I crunched it. My thoughts, as now you may judge, were all introverted, as the saying is;

and you may call it self-pity, or the sense of frustration, or sullen hate of the folly of fools, or any blessed thing that gratifies your well-known ability to peer into the souls of other people, though I am sure you are never guilty of so ill-mannered an extreme—what was I saying? Anyhow, I was not pleased with that morning. It was chill, twilighty, and dubious.

The winter seemed to be in accord with the doings of men; it was their very appropriate setting. The properly constituted authority—you know what I mean, one of the numerous State offices in which is divined what is good for us, against our inferior judgment—doubtless gave this frozen fog priority over less important things months ago, though it was kept secret, until released. A shoe-lace then became loose, as will happen, everybody knows, when fingers are sufficiently numbed. Despite the fog I could see where I was, and rested my foot on a familiar ledge. When this annoyance was adjusted I stood up, and stared indolently at what was before me. Then stared in wonder. Something queer had happened while my attention was downward. I was wrong in supposing I knew my whereabouts. The shrubs that ordinarily are there had gone. Nothing was there as I had known it.

This winter morning was by no means in harmony with our doings. Unlike us, it had space for leisure. It was in a sportive humour. Probably it did not care a snowflake for us. It was about its own affairs, whatever they may be—and it is no good asking—in its world apart, from which I was shut out. Anyhow, I had the instant impression that I was shut out. I could stretch my hand into that world, to verify it, yet the truth of it would always avoid my apprehension, as though it were spectral. It is odd that the modern mind—and I suppose I have one, of a sort, though its value to up-to-date technology cannot be worth examination—the modern mind, I say, with its faith in exact measurements, a matter of life or death to it, rarely surmises that its calculations, which work perfectly well, and therefore are correct, are only tricks for trumpery ends, and that its serious devotion to the testing of the means to its purpose may be cock-eyed to the immeasurable purpose which keeps blacked-out London suspended among the lights between Capella and Canopus. It is beginning to appear as if the more our laboratories and test tubes tell us, the more phenomena we name and measure, the less our understanding; for did men ever know as much as they do this year, and was their understanding ever less?

I cannot tell you. All I know is that when I stood up, and saw what was immediately before me, there was a shock to my small certainties. I was even a little fearful, very like the savage alone and the silent trees about him. It was as if, glancing carelessly at an ancient house, vacant these many years, and said only by the vulgar to be haunted, I saw at a window, just for a moment, a face looking at me.

Don't ask me what I mean. I have no measurement for it. If we tried to find words for some of the ideas that faintly show and vanish, our friends might think we were not quite at our best. Let us leave these conjectures to the musicians. I can only say lamely that hoar-frost was up to its pranks. The sprays and branches of a dingy suburban enclosure were elaborated into a fantastic white florescence. The buds in this garden were diamonds and what not. There were wild ornaments and fandangles where I had seen nothing before, worth looking at. The pales and rails of an old fence were of a classical purity calling for preservation; it was a standard for elegance. It was the best news that had come my way for a long time.

What chance little things they are, that confirm the private thoughts we hardly dare to express to a friend, unless sure of him, and the hour is right! I remember, when very young, that I came to a tree at the bottom of our street. It had to be passed daily; a train a bit further on had to be caught. That tree never had anything to say to me. But on this morning it had. It must have had a touch of the sun. It was a bird-cherry, and at that moment an astonishing mixture of white and pale translucent green, with rosy chaffinches darting among its pendulous flowers. I stopped, and lost the train. Worse still, I did not go dutifully to the office that day, according to rule and destiny. Somebody nudged me from my ancestry, for destiny was mocked. I went to Selborne instead, and loafed all day in the neighbourhood of The Wakes, I don't know why. There can be no reason for it, anyhow, that would satisfy a magistrate. It is long years ago; and what treasure, if any, I missed at the office is forgotten, but I can still get into the light of that gay morning, when I want to. The spirit of that day without a date has been of help to me since, when I disliked the look of Destiny.

The frost did not hold for long, after all. The old fence lost its elegance in a night. There was a thaw, and we were back on the news of war. We cannot keep our best moments with us all the week. The cold shadow of man is so liable to get between us and the sun. It was thawing. The air had gone southerly, and it prompted me to look—a foolish impulse—to the end of the garden; but the end of it, untrodden for months, was still as deep and unapproachable as the winter before last. Since the transforming white geometry of the frost had gone, I could note that the last gale had blown away a young apple tree. But the tree could wait. There was plenty of time yet before the earth's warm juice would begin to rise. Lots of winter and war to come!

Yet it was a decided thaw, soft and deep. It was mild and persuasive. We were getting on. You could be sure of good, as well as of evil. The feel of it made me unreasonably cheerful. I went out to experience this new mildness. It is enough to incline us to happiness, the surprise that a better thing, un-invited because we were unaware of its existence, is with us, is in the house, when we were prepared to endure its opposite for an unknown period. I noticed that the low black hill in the west had beyond it a promise of about another half-hour's amber day, for the sun had set.

In a dusky thicket at the cross-roads, a thrush was soliloquizing. He fell silent as I arrived. I had paused to listen, for his voice reminded me of something, and I wished to remember what it was. It was something pleasant, yet did not suggest a name. As I stopped, so did the thrush. Then tentatively, as if the windless silence itself began to thaw, and moved in a thin and easy trickle, that bird tried over again his acceptance of his scene. His acceptance was ready, and flowed freely. He was at peace with his thicket. There was no problem in his voice. Night was already on the ground, and had risen into the tree where he was. It was a tall holly, and the top of it was ramified distinctly against the last of light in the sky; and there he sat, hunched up, apparently singing in his sleep. His dreaming was like that. A few of the stars were out.

So I went home. There was nothing more to do. I could not expect to get more out of one day. It was not the time for work—the thaw did not suggest work, but release. It was not the time to read, either. My books did not look as right as the black pinnacle of a holly patterned near a star. Though what the good was in that tree, for it encumbers an eligible building site, I'm not sure. Perhaps, for a moment only, it was a thing in itself, as an art critic would say, and my luck was to see it that way for the first time. There was no certainty about it, nothing real, except that you could go out many times, and search piously for it, and fail to find it. Nobody knows why such things happen as they do.

There is no reason in it, according to the nature of reason, any more than a thrush has reason when sure of his tree and his hour. He never knows what he is doing, but responds thoughtlessly when the evening is bright and liquid. My thrush was unaware of the news known to me. He could only publish all the news known to him. On that bare hill, from which the last of the day had now gone, men once lived—so the learned tell us—who used flint arrow-heads; and I expect the thrush paused then, as one of the neolithics passed by, as he did when I came along; but that other man was hurrying home with the grave tidings of the coming of strangers with bronze spears. To-day, electric pylons are on that hill, an aerodrome is near, and motor roads, yet the thrush has not learned any more; he is satisfied with the news he has.

Still, though irrational, he is also disturbing. He had taken the gist out of my books, for one thing. For there are odd moments when a hint does come of a reality hitherto fabulous, of a truth that may be everlasting, yet is contrary to all our experience. When the night is still, and the problems to be solved are such as we have, and cannot be denied, a suggestion of that kind, when one is alone, is enough to make terrible, as well as ridiculous, the compulsions which keep society earnest and laborious, but unhappy. What would happen if such a suggestion were dwelt upon? To what would it lead? I do not know. But it does seem hard that our earth may be a far better place that we have yet discovered, and that peace and content may be only round the corner, yet that somehow our song of praise is prevented; or does not go well with Hesperus, unlike that of a silly bird.

André Maurois

LIKE SANTA CLAUS

"BERTRAND," said Isabelle, "you remember the smart little Frenchwoman in the lift the other day? You know—you remember the hat, obviously a Paris model. Well, her name is Madame Jacques Leuwen. Her husband's a French officer and he's been a prisoner of war in Germany since May 1940. She's a refugee, came to New York with her little girl. An aunt, who's married to an American, is looking after them."

"Isabelle, you're wonderful—you would have made a marvellous police inspector. . . . Who's told you all this?"

"Ethel the chamber-maid. . . . Madame Leuwen has a flat on the floor above, and Ethel does the 23rd and 24th, and she says the little girl is a darling."

"It's truly remarkable how interested you are in strangers."

"Oh, but this case *is* interesting. Fancy! the little girl has never seen her father; no, never. She was born just after he was taken prisoner; it's November now, 1944, she must be four and a half. It reminds me of the London children who've been born since the black-out—they've never seen the streets lit up. This child has no idea of family life . . . her idea of a home is a room in an hotel. Ethel's sentimental, and tells me it's rather pathetic the way Madame Leuwen surrounds the child with photographs of her Daddy, so that he will be part of her life. Besides, we have mutual friends in Paris. The Leuwens are relations of your friend Denise Holman. . . . Next time I see her I shall speak to her."

Isabelle introduced herself the next day to Odette Leuwen, and was invited to tea at No. 24D. She came back more enthusiastic than ever. "You ought to come up with me, Bertrand."

"I? You know very well that children bore me."

"You won't be bored with Jacqueline. She is amazingly intelligent, quite grown up at four, and a perfect little actress, really charming, and such a little flirt . . . and she sings and dances and she's beginning to read and knit."

"Four years old! And what, pray, does she read?"

"You really do amuse me, Bertrand. You're a typical author, just as she's a typical little woman. I'm telling you about a child aged four, and your first question is 'What does she read?' . . . My dear Bertie, she's not got as far as *La Chartreuse* yet, or *Le Cote de chez Swann* . . . but you *will* like talking to her mother . . . It's very touching . . . very much in love with her husband, absolutely faithful, but nevertheless, after five years of war, very tired of the loneliness. In this country where all the women, married or not, live such a life of freedom, do you think it's easy for someone so young and attractive to deny herself everything?"

"I see no reason why she shouldn't have a bit of fun."

"*You* mightn't, but her husband might . . . she doesn't want to risk some clumsy idiot writing something to him in a letter and upsetting him. . . . Think of the wretched man in an *Oflag*, not enough to eat, ill-treated, with nothing to do, his only interest in life to get back to his wife and child . . . and think of when he does come home. . . . She wants to keep herself just for him, even her thoughts. . . . She's keeping a diary for him to read later on—it's really beautiful."

A few days later she managed to drag Bertrand up to No. 24D. Jacqueline immediately showed off a thousand and one little tricks for his benefit, climbed on his knees, made him tell her a story, put on the gramophone by herself and danced to the music, and recited a fable with appropriate mime and gesture. "A perfect little Frenchwoman," was Bertrand's verdict. "I thoroughly approve, Madame, of your way of bringing her up. You must find it difficult to keep up the French atmosphere here."

"It isn't easy," replied Madame Leuwen. "She occupies my time completely from morning till night. But I am so anxious that her Daddy, when he actually does see her, shall find her just as he imagines her—and also, I try to make *him* as real to her as possible. I read bits of his letters to her. . . . Oh, Jacqueline, tell Mr. Schmitt about the camp."

As they left, Bertrand turned to his wife. "You're right, it's rather pathetic, the idea of the absent one always present . . and I love the little girl."

"Naturally, after the way she made love to you! I knew she would appeal to you . . . but I like the mother better . . . she's more natural. The child's too much of an actress. I wonder if you noticed that she recited her father's letters as if she were repeating ' The Grasshopper and the Ant '? "

"Isabelle, I believe you're jealous."

A day or two before Christmas, Isabelle met Madame Leuwen in the hall loaded with mysterious parcels wrapped in bright paper and tied with gold ribbon. "Jacqueline not with you to-day? " she asked. "No, I left her with my Aunt for an hour or two; I wanted to do some shopping and buy her a few presents. I don't want the war to make her miss all the little pleasures of childhood. My Aunt and I are going to decorate a little Christmas tree for her . . . as a matter of fact, I was going to ask you . . . would you both like to come up for a few minutes when we light the candles? I should be so pleased, and I'm sure you would enjoy seeing her in such a happy mood."

"We shall be delighted . . . you know, my husband has quite fallen in love with your little girl."

"Yes, and she's fallen for him, too. She said to me, ' Oh, isn't he nice, the M'sieu from 23D.' "

"It's usually mutual, love at first sight! . . . Yes, we'd love to come, and we'll bring some little presents."

E

"They will be very welcome: I'm afraid it will be a poor Christmas in spite of all I can do—I've no one in New York except my Aunt, and her time's taken up with her good works and her clubs and societies. . . . I'll expect you then, but please bring only small things. They give a child as much pleasure as expensive ones—and after all, we're only refugees."

The Christmas tree was a real Christmas tree, not an artificial skeleton encrusted and powdered with hoar frost and and hung with red and blue electric lights. Madame Leuwen had carefully arranged about it the mysterious packages, which said: "From Daddy." . . . "With love from Grandmama." . . "From Aunt Cicely." . . . "To Jacquotte from Mummy."

Jacqueline paused in her contemplation of these wonders. "The tree, Mummy, and all the candles and the silver trimmings, who brought it?"

"Father Christmas, darling."

"Who *is* Father Christmas, Mummy?"

"Why, you saw him just now dear, in the street, with his red cloak and white beard and a bell in his hand."

"Oh, yes, Ethel calls him Santa Claus. . . . But, Mummy, there *is* no Santa Claus. . . . It's only a fairy tale."

"But, darling, you saw him yourself."

"Oh, that's only someone dressed up. *I* know—*you* bought the Christmas tree, and you left me with Auntie to hide it.

"Well, why do you ask me—if you know?"

"Just to see what you would say. . . ."

The great moment came to open the parcels. Bertrand had sent her picture books; Isabelle's parcel contained a cradle with four dolls all alike and all asleep—the Quadruplets. Mummy had given her a model of the Eiffel Tower, and Daddy's present was a white fur cap.

"Mummy, how *could* Daddy send me a present?"

"I suppose he must have written to Santa Claus."

Jacqueline threw a precocious little wink in Bertrand's direction and shrugged her shoulders. Madame Leuwen had opened a bottle of sparkling wine. They drank to France, to Victory, and to Daddy's homecoming. Bertrand and Isabelle took their leave and went below to their flat. About eight o'clock the telephone bell rang.

" Oh, don't answer, Bertrand—pretend we're out."

He took up the receiver, listened for a moment then answered, " Not at all, yes, do come down."

" Are you crazy, Bertrand, who on earth are you inviting to come in at this hour? "

" It's Madame Leuwen, she wants to know if she may come down for a little while, she's feeling depressed."

The door-bell rang almost immediately. " Do forgive me," Madame Leuwen apologised. " This loneliness on Christmas Eve—it's horrible. . . ." She hesitated a moment then went on, " And to make it worse, little Jacqueline said something just as she was going to sleep that upset me terribly—quite innocently of course. . . ." She paused, then, sighing, said quietly, " When I bent down to kiss her, she put her lips close to my ear and whispered to me, ' Now I'm a big girl, Mummy, you can tell me the truth . . . Daddy, he's not real is he, he's just a make-believe, like Santa Claus? '."

Eiluned Lewis

THE HOLY INNOCENTS

ARE they still there, Della Robbia's children?
You saw them across the dusty square,
As the tram clanked by to Fiesole,
Through the warm Etruscan air,
On the hospital walls, those famous few,
The small white figures against the blue.

I think the old sculptor—Luca or Andrea—
Chose his models some soft springtide
When Giotto's tower was new and shining
And children played along Arno side.
He chose the loveliest babies of all,
Giovanni, Benito, Francesco and Paul,
And there they are, most gentle and wise,
With flower-sweet faces and dreaming eyes.

But all that happened so long ago,
Before the world's young laughter was spent;
A Florentine mother would bring her babe
To pose as a Holy Innocent,
When the warm sun shone and the blossom was bright,
A picture for ever in blue and white.

O sweet, wise children in swaddling wraps,
Forever waiting with outstretched hands,
Waiting until man's eyes are opened,
Waiting until he understands
That the best the best of us knows, by far,
Can only be learnt where children are.

Now the sunlight is drowned in darkness,
Herod sits once more on his throne.
Stop your ears from the sound of weeping,
Rachel wild-eyed weeps for her own,
For the Innocents slain who lie at our door,
Whose tender April shall come no more,
For the broken buds and the heavy guilt,
For the fairest gift of Heaven spilt.

HOUSE IN BERKELEY SQUARE

Rachel Reckitt

Vera Brittain

MÜTTERCHEN

OUTSIDE the curtained windows of the Children's Home at Sterndale Spa, the snow was falling with stealthy precision on the Derbyshire hills. As Elsie Stevenson put out the light in the big dormitory where the homeless orphans from a dozen war-stricken countries formed a miniature Society of Nations, a shrill chorus of boys' voices followed her excitedly.

"Good-night, Madam! Merry Christmas! To-morrow I'll show you what Santa Claus puts in my stocking!"

Close to the door little Felix, the youngest and newest arrival at the Home, turned his head as she passed. The three-year-old son of Austrian Jews who had fled from Vienna when Hitler arrived there in 1938, he was too young consciously to miss the father and mother who had both perished when a flying bomb descended on Golders Green. By the light of her torch she could see his large dark eyes shining with the innocent devotion of a small affectionate child.

"*Gute Nacht . . . Mütterchen,*" he murmured sleepily.

"Good-night, Felix," she responded, a sudden dimness blurring the electric bulb in the passage as she closed the door. "*Mütterchen,*" he had called her, though she had come there only as the Matron who mended the boys' much-torn clothes, and supervised their boisterous manners. Did the word perhaps mean that, out of the void in her own heart, she had made a success of her job?

As she switched on the light in her sitting-room at the end of the corridor, her eyes fell as usual on the photographs of Dinah and Jim, standing side by side on the mantelpiece. Next week it would be four years since they left her—they and the others. She lit the gasfire and picked up the sock that she was knitting for twelve-year-old Pieter from Holland, but her mind dwelt, with the intensity always forced upon her by the coming of Christmas, on the events of that night at Ketford four Decembers ago.

After the long strain of the autumn raids which smote London in 1940, she and Jim had decided to go north and spend Christmas week with her mother and sisters. Ketford was on the edge of industrial Lancashire, but though, wrote her mother, they had the sirens when enemy bombers went to Manchester or Liverpool, nothing had ever fallen on their own little town, and they felt perfectly safe there. Couldn't she and Jim allow themselves a bit of a break? They could guess what those months of bombing must have meant to a doctor and his wife in the centre of Fulham.

Mother's intuition had been right, of course. Neither she nor Jim had written a word about the nights when he went out into lurid darkness to crawl under the wreckage of houses with his hypodermic syringe, while she waited alone listening to the crash of bombs, now far, now near . . . but Mother had guessed. So Elsie persuaded Jim to take the short holiday, and on their way they had collected Dinah from her boarding-school in Bedfordshire. Elsie could picture her little daughter's laughing eager face as she waited for them at the end of the school drive, her tam-o'-shanter set rakishly on her straight fair hair, and her suitcase, filled to bursting point with Christmas presents for the family, tied insecurely together with string.

Of course they had never intended to send her to boarding-school when she was only eleven, but the war and the raids on London made the decision inevitable. She was doing very well, though, for she was a clever child—more like her aunts Helen and Norah, who both came home from their respective teaching posts the day before Elsie arrived at Ketford with Jim and Dinah. She herself had been the lowbrow member of the family; but she never regretted her more homely qualities when she looked back on her training as a nurse at Bart's, and the secret meetings with Jim who was then walking the hospitals.

It had been a happy week, for they were always a united family, and Dinah, as usual, was a perpetual source of irrepressible vitality. But no one could have called the nights restful, with heavy raids on Manchester just before Christmas, and the frequent alerts followed almost immediately by the overhead bumping of the Nazi bombers. Elsie, half awake beside Jim, who ignored the noise and went promptly to sleep, listened with the uneasy remorse familiar to the inhabitants of raided cities who realise that this time the trouble is destined for somebody else. Evening after evening she listened—until the night before they were due to return to London . . . In her room at Sterndale Elsie shivered, crouching closer to the gasfire as she recalled the reverberating roar which obliterated the dying echo of the siren, heard the crash of masonry tumbling into the room, and remembered her dazed half-awareness of the blow that plunged her into depths beyond darkness.

Some time afterwards—she had never known whether it was minutes or hours—she returned to the momentary consciousness of excruciating headache and a feeling of unbearable cold. She tried to move, but a heavy weight on her left shoulder pinned her down. From a distance that seemed aeons away, she heard a muttered injunction : " Careful, Sam ! I believe this un's alive." Then she drifted back into welcome oblivion, emerging at last to find herself wrapped in blankets on a stretcher in the chill murky daylight. Gradually she became conscious of noise, chaos, confusion; of the rubble-strewn pavement outside her mother's house, and the grim element of order introduced by the waiting line of official vehicles. Her left shoulder felt stiff and bruised, but the sense of confining weight was gone. A W.V.S. volunteer handed her a cup of tea from a mobile canteen, and as she drank it she looked up to see the pale, concerned face of her uncle, George Tompkins, her mother's youngest brother who went daily from Ketford to his solicitor's office in Stockport.

Restored now to full awareness, she cried aloud in sudden terror: "Uncle George, where's Dinah? Where's Jim? What's happened to Mother and Norah and Helen?" And she perceived with increased apprehension how the concern and embarrassment deepened in her uncle's face as he replied evasively: "Look here, Elsie . . . you've been knocked about a bit. You'd better go along to the First Aid Post and let them have a look at you. If you're all right, I'll help you to the Rest Centre . . . Kitty and Tim are there already. We had a bit of bomb damage ourselves."

He did not tell her that he and his wife and schoolboy son had left their roofless and windowless house at dawn to seek shelter with Elsie's mother.

"At least Mildred will take us in for a bit and give us some breakfast," he had said. But when they reached the familiar street it was worse damaged than his own, and in the road, close to shapeless piles of rubble which had once been homes, stood an ominous queue of A.R.P. ambulances. A Warden, recognizing him, seized him by the arm.

"I shouldn't go down there, Mr. Tompkins," he had said. But George, leaving his family with the Warden, had gone all the same. . . .

Raising herself on her right elbow, Elsie gazed at him blankly. "The Rest Centre! What for?" she asked.

"Well, there's nothing left of the house . . . We can stay at the Centre till we've decided where to go."

"But I can't go to the Rest Centre without Dinah!"

"She'll be all right," he said awkwardly. "They'll bring her along." And then, to his relief, the stretcher-bearers reached Elsie, lifted her protesting into an ambulance, and drove her off to the First Aid Post. There, finding no bones broken, they had treated her for shock.

It was not until the afternoon, lying on a couch in the crowded Rest Centre which she recognized as the local Friends' Meeting House, that she learned the truth from Uncle George. Even then, his words had seemed at first to be counterfeit tokens, devoid of significance. Only very gradually had their terrible meaning captured her understanding.

"Not all gone . . . Uncle, not *all*? Not Dinah *and* Jim? Not Mother and Norah and Helen . . . ? "

She did not add: "After all we've been through in London!" But the bitter irony of those successive risks endured unscathed hammered at her imagination through the nightmare fog of unreality from which her Uncle spoke.

"I'm sorry, Elsie. I'd a thousand times rather have gone myself than have to tell you. . . . But you were the only one found alive in the house."

She must, she thought, have been kept under drugs that night, for all recollection of it had completely vanished. But the next morning remained starkly etched on the tablets of her memory—the grotesque morning in which she and her uncle had sought the bodies of their relatives through the hastily improvised mortuaries in the stricken town.

"If you don't find them at the Hospital or the Baptist chapel, you'd better try the Market, Mr. Tompkins," said the head of the Rest Centre. "We never expected anything like this in Ketford," he added. "Two hundred killed found yesterday, and thirty more since dawn to-day. The rescue workers are at their wits' end to know where to take them."

For an hour, she recalled, they had stood in the queue of pale-faced mourners waiting to identify their dead in the covered Market, and then Uncle George, who knew the local undertakers, had made his way in with one of their representatives. As she waited, leaning dizzily against the stall where week after week her mother had purchased carrots and potatoes, she had hungered with a dreadful frantic hunger for one more glimpse of Dinah's face, before the earth covered her wide blue eyes and sweet blunt nose, and hid the soft fair hair which Elsie had brushed in front of the fire on winter evenings before the War. . . . But when Uncle George came out, white and shaken, he took her firmly by the arm and led her back to the Rest Centre in spite of her entreaties and, at last, her tears.

" No, Elsie. You don't know what it's like in there. It's better to remember Dinah and Jim as you knew them. . . ."

At the mass funeral attended by half the town, she had been fretted, she remembered, because everybody talked to her about her mother's goodness, and the loss Helen would be to the High School, but nobody even mentioned Jim. . . . Dr. Stevenson would be mourned by humble men and women in the monotonous streets of West Kensington and Hammersmith, but he had been almost unknown in Ketford. That day of burials, she thought, had marked the moment at which she lost all her initiative. Mechanically she learned that Uncle George had taken a new house at Cheete, in Staffordshire; automatically she accepted his invitation to remain with him and Kitty until she had made some new plan for living. It was only when they had moved to Cheete that a less harassed doctor discovered the deep-seated injury to her left shoulder, and she faced the fact that she would never again be able to lift a bed-ridden patient, nor be fit for her old profession of hospital nursing.

" Why was I left when they were taken? Why? Why? " she had cried out bitterly.

And her Uncle's wife, a shy but religious woman who had attended the Meetings of the Friends at Ketford, had urged her diffidently to remember the mysterious ways of Providence.

" The Lord's got a job waiting for you somewhere, Elsie, even if it isn't quite the one you trained yourself to do."

She hadn't believed Kitty, of course. But four months later, sitting convalescent in the garden on a warm summer afternoon, and glancing listlessly through the *Manchester Courier*, she had seen the advertisement.

"Wanted for Children's Home in Derbyshire, resident Matron to supervise 40 small boys, refugees from Europe, orphaned by the air raids. Good salary and own sitting-room. Nursing experience desirable. Apply, stating age and qualifications, to the Secretary, International House, Tor Hill, Sterndale Spa."

Elsie put down the paper and stared, unseeing, over the sunlit garden. "Forty small boys, refugees from Europe, orphaned by the air raids. . . ." The words had opened a door in her mind which hitherto had been no more than ajar; they precipitated her into one of those moments of insight which leave life profoundly and permanently changed.

Before the raid on Ketford, she had perceived the war almost exclusively as it affected herself and Dinah and Jim. Like the inhabitants of other raided cities on both sides of the battle line, she had endured the bombardment of London with no pretensions to heroism. The busy doctor's household repre-sented her work and the centre of her life; she had "taken" the raids because she had no alternative. She was kind, of course, to her neighbours in Fulham, reassuring them in the shelters, and helping them to evacuate their young sons and daughters. But she had neither sought nor realized any kin-ship with those unknown mothers and children, the helpless and innocent victims of war, who throughout the world shared her experience; whose terrors and endurances were one with her own. . . .

Gazing at the laurel bushes which marked the end of her uncle's garden, she seemed as in a waking vision to perceive the stupendous tragedy of wartime motherhood, broken, bereft, and like Rachel finding no place of comfort; to understand the bewildered agony of wartime childhood, starved, orphaned, left to wander uncherished in a dumb, animal-like quest for food and shelter. Her own darling had died unacquainted with grief . . . but sorrow and fear had been from their babyhood the pitiless companions of those young refugees from Europe who had never known security. Hounded from city to city, from country to country, their brief experience of home and shelter among strangers had been cruelly ended by that same universal misuse of science which had annihilated her own happiness. But she, at least, had known twelve years of unforgettable family life. Could she, having golden memories which she would hold fast for ever, really count herself bereft in comparison with these children who would grow to manhood without the recollection of country or parents or home?

Half dazed by the sudden widening of her mental and spiritual perspective, she picked up the fallen newspaper and read the advertisement again. Surely there was no one who could give to a motherless child the same love and understanding as a childless mother? Two sorrows put together would not make joy—but they might, perhaps, add up to consolation. . . .

The gong sounded for tea, and Elsie sprang from her chair like a drowner in deep water who suddenly pushes through the suffocating waves to fresh air and sunlight. Forgetting the stiffness of her arm and shoulder, she crossed the lawn with a lightness of step which banished finally the heavy languor of the months since December.

"Why, Elsie!" exclaimed her uncle's wife with observant pleasure, "How much better you're looking to-day!"

"I feel much better. . . . Do you know, Kitty, I believe you were right. I think I've found the job that was meant for me!"

And as, eagerly, she held out the newspaper, she began mentally to compose the letter that she would write after tea.

"Dear Sir, I beg to apply for the post, advertised in the *Manchester Courier*, of Resident Matron at International House in Sterndale Spa . . ."

Henry Williamson

THE ACKYMALS

ONE full-summer afternoon, following a stormy night, when the shadows of the walls and thatch lay sharply on the drying road, a shot rang out in the hollow of the village, and a little boy walking in the shade past the nettles growing out of the wall of Hole Farm, stopped, and said to himself, "Coo! I bet that one knacked'n vlying!"

"Hullo, Ernie," I called from my window, glad of any excuse to leave my desk. "What's been knocked flying?"

"'Tis Janny Kift shooting th'ackymals on his pays!"

I ran out of the room, and down the steps to the road, crying, "So that is what has been startling my baby, day after day! Why does that fool want to shoot tomtits? They don't eat peas. They eat insects on the peas. Poor little tomtits. Would you shoot an ackymal, Ernie?"

"I ain't got no gun," murmured Ernie.

"That's why the eleven nestlings in the hole in my garden wall died this spring! He shot the old birds."

"When Janny Kift finds an ackymal's nestie, he blocks'n up if he can't tear'n out. Father see'd'n doing it. Be 'ee gwin to the funeral?"

"What funeral, Ernie?"

"They be gwin to bury a babby up to churchyard this afternoon. I be gwin. Be you gwin?"

When he is quiet, Ernie's face has an expression that rests in beauty; his brown eyes brim with a sweet and gentle luminousness, as though a spirit were looking forth from the eyes of a child.

" Us be gwin," said Ernie.

I remembered hearing about the baby. Four days before, a treble toll of the bell in the church tower had brought the cottage wives to their doors. After an interval, a single toll; and the women had waited, to learn the age of the dead child. The bell was silent. One year old! Then Mrs. Ridd's babby were dead, poor li'l mite.

The swallows were twittering over the village street, and the martins were busy with their late brood in the nest over the door of Hole Farm. The black and white droppings, remains of thousands of flies, splashed the wall and the sett-stones under, every year, for the farmer " liked seeing the birds about ". No, I was not going to the funeral.

Ernie knew all about death, although probably he had forgotten what he had told me three years before, when he was four. Graves he called pits. Before burial, dead men " had a good tea first, and then they take their boots off and put them in pits. They can't see nobody any more when they be in the pits, because the earth be in their eyes." I remembered asking him, trying to probe the child-mind, how he would like to be buried; but he had shaken his head, saying he " won't never go into a pit, because he can't never die." Asked how he knew that, Ernie said, " Jesus said so," and told me that it was in Sunday School. Later, his mother had told me that Ernie had been shown a biblical picture of the disciples walking through a cornfield, shod with sandals, and eating corn; and this had made the above impression on his mind.

The Lower House stood at the top of Church Street, where it joined the road to Windwhistle Cross and beyond. Passing the carpenter's cottage and shed, with its large enamelled iron Navy Recruiting advertisement, lime-washed after the War with the rest of the wall, I reached the sunken thatched cottage where John Kift lived. " Plaise to come right in, midear," invited Mrs. John Kift, an elderly plump woman, dressed in black clothes smelling of moth-ball. " Mind 'ee don't brish

against they walls; they'm spotty as a leper. 'Tis the damp,
zur. No matter what be done, they walls remain spotty as a
leper!" I stepped down into a damp, dark passage, and into
a darker living room, lit by a small square window. A
percussion-cap single-barrel gun was laid on two rusty nails
driven into the great oaken beam crossing the smoky ceiling;
the beam, as in all the cottages, had been lime-washed. I noticed
photographs on the high chimney piece, and bunches of herbs
drying along the beam; and then I heard the craking voice of
John Kift calling me from the end of the passage.

At the passage-end were sheds, cluttered with old gins, and
pails, and shovels, and boxes; bedsteads, bicycle frames and
wheels, pea-sticks, and barrels. Rust had worn away the iron
lying there, the death-watch beetle—the " worm " of the
countryman—had bored the wooden supports and rafters.
Cobwebs, loaded with the frass of the boring insects, and with
mummied moths and flies and wasps, filled the upper spaces
of the sheds. John Kift stood beside a box with a wire net
front, behind the webs of which a ferret was moving, trying
to get out. " You shoot tomtits, what you call ackymals, don't
you? " I asked.

" Aiy aiy! he cried. " Every wan I zee near my pays! I load
me gun with a half-charge, and blow ivry wan of the li'l beggars
abroad! Seventy-eight I've shute this year, and in the spring
my son blocked up half-a-dizen nesties in holes in walls round-
about." His voice grew louder and louder. " Yes, zur! And
if us didden do that, us wouldn't have a pay left, noomye!"

" But tomtits eat insects," I protested.

" And pays as well! Yes, zur! They be master birds for
pays, the rogues! But this one won't ate no more pays." And
with the toe of his boot he kicked a tiny bundle of feathers
lying on the ground. I picked it up. Half its feathers were
blown off its breast, its legs broken, its eyes filmy in its loose and
backward-rolling head. Its neck and head were a deep black—
a marsh tit, weighing, perhaps, half an ounce.

F

John Kift took me to the rows of peas and showed me pods three inches long, with ragged tears along the length of shucks, as though rats had gnawn them. " Knack, knack, knack, the li'l hellers go on them, and I'll shute ivry wan I zee!"

Four kinds of titmice were lying on the ground under the peas—great, blue, coal, and marsh. I knew that great-tits and blue-tits could chip and hack expertly with their strong beaks—the name ackymal or hackmal, and its numerous variations, is derived from the blows they deal—but I was certain of the innocence of the marsh-tits.

" I'll shute ivry beggar I zee on my pays!"

" That's so, zur. John Kift be quite honest, zur," said the rough and pleasant voice of Mrs. Kift behind me.

He agreed to allow the next tit to feed before shooting, and then to bring the slain bird to me for dissection.

" You'll zee I be right, midear," he called after me, as I went into the gloomy passage, wondering what sort of a fool he thought me. I had seen sparrows and finches pecking the fresh green leaves of sprouting peas in early spring, for I had seen them walking down my own rows, and had thrown stones near them. What business was it of mine if birds slew peas, and a man slew the birds? Slugs and snails ate my seedling cabbages, and I burned them with quick-lime; but John Kift did not interfere with me for it. Was this feeling of pity for little happy birds shot in the sunshine an unnatural feeling, arising from discarded instincts; a useless feeling, as unproductive as a rainbow? Thought made me miserable.

The village street was bright and quiet. I noticed a hand drawing a curtain across a window. A girl ran past the gate, saying in a loud whisper, " They'm coming," and hustling a young sister into a cottage. The old terrier called the Mullah lying at the bend in the road by the shop got up, scratched, stared at something invisible to me, and sauntered away. I heard a shuffling of feet. Then round the corner came four youths, clad all in black, except for white bow-ties and white collars and white gloves. They moved very slowly, carrying a small white coffin on two cloth slings, one at each end. I saw blackness behind them, and hurried away.

Women were standing by the low churchyard wall, looking over the green mounds, and I stood among them, next to Mrs. Butt, who immediately told her three little girls—heavy Saxon type—to shut their rattle; and then smiled at me, showing her ruinous teeth. Mrs. Butt's five-month baby, without a stitch on its grubby body or a tooth in its gums, lying in a perambulator near, also smiled. I felt its chubby legs, and remarked how well it looked, but how cold it was in the shadow of the elm trees. "Ah, I likes 'em to be 'ardy," said Mrs. Butt, smiling again, and asking after my baby, who was born on the same night as her own. "Fine li'l boy you've got!" I agree, and smile at the recollection of what Mrs. Butt is reported to have said to the parish nurse when told that her baby was not a boy. "Cor darn, what beats me is where all these girls come from."

"Tikey, get down!" scolds Mrs. Willy Gammon, mother of innumerable children and grandmother of several, to the seven-year-old merry boy who robbed one of my apple trees last year. Tikey laughs, and won't get down; he is the unconquerable sort, nervously and physically strong. Even when I whacked him hard, over that apple business, he didn't whine; but, with angry tears in his eyes, picked up apples and earth and flung them at me, crying, "Ha, 'it 'im agen, wull 'ee? 'It 'im agen, wull 'ee, ye ould booger?" We respected each other afterwards, and I gave him the hazel stick for a souvenir; and now we meet as proper friends.

Daisy is Tikey's younger sister, then comes Boykins, whose round brownish face—all the Gammons have ruddy-brown faces—is still rather scared of me; it was Boykins, aged nearly four, who from the road below tearfully urged Tikey to kick me during the mock whacking. Daisy, red lips and soft brown eyes, regards me from the wall, as she cuddles the Gammon baby, a petulant and spiteful child, aged three, " the last Mrs.

Gammon will have, surely, at her age," says the village. Daisy's face is full of love; the little maid will make a good mother when she weds later on.

So I muse by the wall, whereon many children sit, eager for the sight of a baby's funeral. The bell tolls. Scientists tell us that the bony structure of the bat is nearer to the human frame than any other mammal : and lo! here are great human bats following the coffin with slow and shuffling steps, old women with strange and ugly faces, clothed in black. Their eyes peer under shapeless bonnets; their clothes, like wings of black shrivelled skin, seem to suffocate the personality. Tears drip out of their old eyes. They walk into the graveyard, and follow the parson into the church. Only then does Grannie Carter dare to call out, in a loud threatening whisper :

" You come away from that grave, my boy! Young reskle, you! A-a-ah! You wait till I catch 'ee!"

" Ya-ar, ould booger! " cries a minute urchin playing alone by the small shallow grave. He does not care for his grannie, whose voice, harsh and broken, has just threatened him over the wall. The young rascal has blue eyes and a split lip; his toe-caps are kicked broken. His widowed grandmother looks after him; her daughter is in service in another part of the country, and rarely comes home. He is Ernie's cousin, and was christened Vivian Somerville Carter; but Ernie and his friends call him Babe. What a temper Babe had when he was really small, two years or so; when granfer was alive, and used to shut him up in a shed! Dreadful screams of rage! " A very backward baby," his grannie said to me once. " Two and a half year old and 'a can't talk yet. All 'a can do is to swear." But now he goes to school, and plays and fights with other boys, and is happy.

The mourners were in the church; the curious were looking over the wall; the bad boy was sitting by the shallow grave. He was scratching at the earth with his nails and trying to push something into a hole.

" A-a-ah, you young limb!" scolded old Grannie Carter over the wall.

" Ya-aa-ar, ould booger! 'Ee can't catch I now!" taunted Vivian Somerville. He was planting a kidney bean in the earth by the grave.

The grave was twelve feet from the wall. Like all the other graves, it lay west and east—the tiny feet would lie towards the east, awaiting the coming of Christ beyond the sunrise. By one of the trunks of the great elms many wreaths of flowers were laid, piled one on another, each with a card and lines of sympathetic writing; for the baby's death had touched many hearts. A red-haired man stood by them, copying the inscriptions into a penny notebook : he was the village correspondent of the local newspaper, which would describe the flowers as " a wealth of floral tributes ", and for every name included in his list he would probably sell a copy on the following Thursday. He used to keep a motor-car, plying for hire in summer when the visitors came : but the red omnibuses took the visitors, his car grew shabby and out of date; he became a labourer again, and his little boy took round papers, for times were bad.

The children on the wall were merry and noisy as the starlings on the church tower. Grannie Carter stole into the churchyard, grey and lumbering as a badger; but Babe saw her, and with a shrill laugh ran away among the tombs. " Ya-aa-ha! Ye can't catch I naow! Ye can't catch I naow!" he taunted her, waiting for the intense delight of being chased, and plucking at his middle. " Ould Granmer Carter, ye can't catch I!"

Granmer Carter retreated, for something white had appeared out of the church porch, between the stone heads of the gargoyles, one chipped and frowning, the other whole and serene. The Rector, in his vestments, walked slowly, with composed face, his hands clasped before him. Behind, the youths bearing the coffin, and the black straggling files of mourners. Vivian Somerville gave a startled look and ran out of the churchyard.

Children on the wall were pulled down by their mothers, or hushed into silence.

Slowly the mourners settled round the grave. The father was a tall man, with a face yellow as tallow, and a black moustache; a thatcher by trade. He swayed, and looked in the grave, with dull, dry eyes. The face of his remaining child, a youth of eighteen, was also sallow, but puffy with weeping. The old grandfather stood beside the grandmother; sometimes he gulped, like the grandson, and stared wildly as the priest recited, in a low and placid voice, the words of the Church of England Burial Service.

"Man that is born of a woman hath but a short time to live . . ." the mother, shrunken in black mourning, gave a whimpering cry—". . . and is full of misery. He cometh up, and is cut down, like a flower; he fleeth as it were a shadow, and never continueth in one stay."

The parson spoke without feeling. No beauty bloomed in his words, to raise an image in the minds around him. He was sixty years old, and looked forty; perhaps if he had been deeply moved by all the services for burial he had conducted he would have looked eighty. A heavy trundling sound, and the far-away singing of many voices, caused some of the women by the wall to look northwards; children's faces followed their gaze. Round the corner of the Rectory wall came a big yellow motor coach, filling the roadway, and the singing grew suddenly loud. The service went on. A hatless man stood with his back to the driver, conducting the choir with his hands. Dust swirled behind the coach, which quickly slowed, and as it rolled past the burial place the voices sank, but did not die away. The Welsh miners on holiday were singing one of their grand and inspiring national choruses; eyes were brightened when they had passed, except the sad ones by the grave.

As the coffin was being lowered, the mother uttered stifled whimpers, while she stared as though penetrating the white composition of the lid, to the small pale face within. She clutched her husband, longing to fling herself down to break the shut lid and to take the little one, whose every laugh and wail and cry in life were still part of her living heart. She heard words, well-worn words, that since childhood had never entered her consciousness: words, "O Lord God, holy and most merciful Saviour, Lord most holy, O God most mighty, O holy and merciful Saviour." She tried secretly to smile to herself, and whimpered, "I believe, I believe;" while her husband held her tightly, his face a duskier yellow.

Zip-chee-chee. See-see, see-see! A family of marshtits flittered in the shadowed leaves over us, restless and happy as they peered and lit on the twigs, hanging head-down to peer with bright eyes for green-fly and caterpillar.

"Earth to earth, ashes to ashes, dust to dust; in sure and certain hope of the Resurrection to eternal life, through our Lord Jesus Christ; Who shall change our vile body, that it may be like unto His glorious body, according to the mighty working, whereby He is able to subdue all things to Himself."

Sit-ee sit-ee sit-ee! A coal-tit was wandering with them. I could see the streak of white on his black head. *Zip-chee zip-chee*, as they passed, some high in the tree, others just above my head. They swung and fluttered, always calling to one another, sometimes peering for hawk or owl on the branches. For days and weeks they had been wandering in the spinneys and orchards and gardens, sleeping in holes in trees, in the eaves of thatch, ivy on walls, warm and together. I saw the parent birds fly over the Lower House to the hollow of gardens beyond; and then I was listening to words that seemed false and unnatural, and harsh to the miserable beings standing black, as though charred, in the summer sunshine.

"We give Thee hearty thanks, for that it hath pleased Thee to deliver this our sister out of the miseries of this sinful world . . ."

After the service, the priest turned to the mother and said, in a voice more like his own, "Do not grieve, Mrs. Ridd.

She is now safe in the arms of Jesus, and one day you will see her there." " Aiy, aiy!" said the old fisherman, the baby's grandfather. " She'm safe i'th' arms of Jesus," and looked at the sky. He walked away, to get a glass of beer, and looked into the sun's face, which dried his tears, and gave strength of life after grief. I heard the report of a gun.

Children scrambled down from the wall, forgetting what they had seen. Observing Vivian Somerville Carter back on the grass by the flowers, I went to him. He was banging ants with a stone, watched by a small quiet boy who wore an enormous cap. This boy was a visitor to the village, and whenever I had seen him, on the sands, in the street, or on his own doorstep, he was wearing the same large cap. He did not play with the boys of the village, but stood about near them; and once, when I had playfully thrown a minute apple at him, he had gone away with injured dignity, and told his father, who had complained to me.

" Don't you feel sorry, Babe, that this poor little baby is dead? " I asked.

" No."

" Would you be sorry to see Ernie laid in a grave? "

" No."

" Wouldn't you cry, Babe? "

" No."

" What, didn't you cry when Granfer died? "

" No. Uncle Bill did. I zeed un going home crying."

Uncle Bill was Ernie's father, called Revvy because, years before, he had worked in the Rectory garden.

" Would you care if I died, Babe? "

" Booger, no!" he replied, furiously digging with his nails.

" Well, then, will you come and live with me, as you are not happy with Granmer? "

" No, I tull 'ee, you bloomin' vule you, no!"

Yes, I was a blooming fool to continue the inquisition; and I continued:

" But, think, Babe. You will have a nice time, go to bed late, have all the apples you want, and go down to the sand-water every day. Won't you? "

Babe called the sea, sand-water.

" Ya-aa-ah-ee! Ould Daddy Wisson!"

I was Ould Daddy Wisson.

" And think, Babe. You will have a nice bed, all to yourself."

Then the large-capped boy joined the conversation.

" I've got a bed of me own where I live, in a big house up to Exeter."

" Ya-aa!" jeered Babe, " It's a poop bed!"

" Vivian Carter," the other solemnly warned him, " remember you are in the churchyard." Five years old, and already matured, thought I; poor little man. Then I saw John Kift look over the wall, and lean his elbows along it. He was the brother of the fisherman, and great-uncle of the dead baby.

" Well, well!" he said to me, in his loud voice, as I stopped by him. " Did ye ever see anything like it? Look at that, now! Look at them all. Well, well! I call that a turrible waste of money, all they flowers." He stared round again, as though unable to realize what he saw. " Well I never. Did 'ee hever zee anything like it now? Pounds and pounds, I reckon, they flowers must have cost. No flowers will bring it back, noomye. Aiy, pounds and pounds. Well, well! Much better to have given the money to the parents. Pounds and pounds, they flowers must have cost. More than all the doctor's bills, I should say."

He put his hand in his pocket, and drew out two dead marsh-tits, which he put on the wall.

" I don't reckon they doctors be much cop," he mused. " Five doctors Liza took the baby to, and all described bottles and bottles of medicine, but with all of them twarnt no gude. No, zur! I reckon she would have done better, and saved money, if she had kep to one doctor, instead of trittin' around from wan to anither, from Crosstree to Town, from Town to

Combe. Tidden no sense in it. What do 'ee think, Mrs. Carter?"

Granmer Carter was looking at the flowers again.

"Poor li'l mite," she croaked, slowly and sadly. "'Tis most butiful flowers I ever did see. 'Tis a loss for the mother, 'tis a loss, and after eighteen year."

"'Twas going on fine the night before, too!" said the cheerful voice of Mrs. Butt, returning with her perambulator and three yellow-haired girls. "Why, only the night before the poor li'l mite died, it ate nearly a plateful of tinned salmon, so Mrs. Smaldon told me."

So small were the bodies of the ackymals, and so strong the fingers of John Kift, that it was a difficult matter to find, among the feathery pieces, the crops of the birds. Vivian and Ernie stood on the iron toe-tips of their boots, to see the interesting *post-mortem*. The gullets were far too small for the passage of a pea; and no green fragments were found in the crops. Nevertheless, John Kift, pointing to minute black specks, cried, "What did I tell 'ee? I knowed I was right! What more could ye want? They ackymals be master rogues for stealin' pays, and I'll shute ivry wan I zee!"

T. Thompson

NURSERY RHYME

THERE is a garden seat at one end of the bowling green known as the aldermanic bench. On it sit the veterans of the village. Nobody under the age of sixty would dare to plank his corduroy trousers on its dark green surface. Behind it is a square of rougher grass, and during the later years of the war it was noticeable that the numbers of very young children playing there increased.

"By gow," said Joe Briggs, "ah've getten a stiff neck wi' trying to watch th' bowlin' an th' child at the same time."

"It is a bit of a job," said Jack Dagnall.

"Ah, don't bother," said Sam Smith. "If there's owt wrong wi' 'em they'll let thee know."

"They will that," said Bill Wellock. "Our Jane's lungs is made o' leather. If ever hoo tak's to singin' hoo'll never need a mike."

"Ah'll tell yo' what," said Joe. "Th' ground seems a lot further off nor it used to do. Ah've found that out now it's my job to mind th' child."

"Aye," said Jack. "It's hard wark beginnin' again. Ah thowt we'd done wi' rearin' childer."

"Tha'rt not ruein', arta?" asked Sam.

"Not a bit," said Jack. "But Ah find it late in th' day to play skippin' rope wi' a five year owd child. Me knees isn't as swivel-jointed as they used to be."

"Think about it," said Bill. "Their fathers is missin' all th' best on 'em. They were babbies when they went away an' when they come back they'll be little girls. It's th' best part ...

seein' 'em grow up ... gradually like ... a new trick ... a fresh word."

" Tha'rt reet about a fresh word," said Jack. " Tha has to mind what tha says in front on 'em. Our child can swear like a trooper."

" If tha doesn't give o'er climbin' up them railin's Ah'll slap thi . . . now Ah towd thee . . . happen tha'll tak' notice o' thi grand-dad now," said Bill. " Come here . . . there's no need to wakken all th' village . . . here . . . let's see if Ah can find thee a toffee. . . . Ah didn' say find all th' lot one . . . they'd eat a mon's height in toffee if tha'd let 'em. Nah wipe thi eyes an' run an' play thee."

" Tha spiles 'em," said Jack.

" Who does? " said Bill.

" Tha does," said Jack.

" What about thee? " said Bill.

" Well," said Jack defensively, " what about me? "

" Tha'rt as bad as anybody," said Bill.

" If it comes to spilin' 'em," said Sam, " we all sup out o' one pot."

" Ah feel sorry for th' little mites," said Joe. " It's a darned shame."

" What is? " said Jack.

" Why," said Joe, " they've never known their fathers."

" Ah wish Ah'd never known mine," said Jack. " He's welly flayed me when he geet his paddy out."

" Ah expect tha desarved it," said Joe.

" If we'd all got what we desarved when we were young," said Jack, " most on us'd never sit down any more."

" Hasta ever hit that child? " said Sam.

" Could tha hit a child whose father's in Burma? " said Jack.

" Ah don't see what that's getten to do wi' it," said Sam.

" That's wheer tha'rt wrong," said Jack. " That child's getten its father's eyes. Look at 'em. Ah once hit its father an' he just looked at me. There were terror an' surprise starin' out at me. He never cried, an' he never said owt. He just looked at me an' there were Christ at th' back of his e'en. His mother carried him to bed an' tears run down me cheeks."

"Tha'rt none fit to handle a child," said Joe. "Tha'rt too soft."

"Thy lad were no trouble to rear," said Jack. "Mine were. There were times when it were touch an' goo. He were in hospital six weeks when he were but three . . . on th' threshold . . . hasta ever seen a child just hoverin' . . . they're so helpless . . . so dependent . . . an' so patient. They just shame us owd uns."

"Mine were a little devil," said Joe. "His mother used to say : ' They make thi arms ache when they're babbies an' they make thi heart ache when they grow up.' But it were nobbut devilment. There were nowt fundamentally wrong about th' lad. He were th' apple o' me eye."

"Didn't he win th' Military Cross? " said Sam.

"He won summat," said Joe. "But Ah'd rather have him back. His child's just like him. He gets me all of a lather. He's too mich for me. He needs a father at back of him."

"What dosta think our child axed me t'other day? " said Bill. "Ah don't know," said Sam. "She wanted to know how they put skins on oranges," said Bill.

"It's read me a story wi' ours," said Sam. "Ah've supped more ale sin' Ah had to mind that child nor ever Ah've done afore. Ah gets as hoarse as an owd crow."

"All th' world's a story to 'em," said Jack. "They live in a land o' make believe. Ah lifted our child to look o'er th' parson's fence an' hoo asked me if it were th' witch's garden."

"Tha'rt reet about make-believe," said Sam. "T'other day our child geet all its dolls out and laid 'em all in a row on th' hearth rug. Ah had to be Doctor Shaw and th' nipper were th' matron an' Ah had to give all th' dolls sun-ray treatment. Ah found one o' them electric bicycle lamps wi' a shade in th' front an' Ah were able to give 'em all a reet dose apiece."

" How did hoo know about sun-ray? " said Jack.

" Hoo had bronchitis when hoo were teethin'," said Sam, " an' they give her sun-ray at th' hospital clinic. They never forget don't childer."

" Forget! " said Joe. " Promise owt an' they'll remind thee."

" Just look at 'em," said Jack. " One's bein' th' father an' one's bein' th' mother. . . . Heigh! . . . tha mustn't hit her wi' that stick. . . . Nah play proper or yo'll ha' to go straight home."

" It tak's thee all thi time to stop 'em feightin'," said Sam.

" Aye," said Joe. " They're just like grown-ups."

" Ah hope they don't ha' to go through what their fathers had to go through," said Jack.

" If it comes to that," said Joe, " Ah hope they don't ha' to go through what their grandfathers had to go through."

" There's summat in that," said Jack. " Stick up for th' lads."

" One thing's sartin," said Bill. " Whate'er comes or goes they'll ha' to live their own lives. All we can do is to pilot 'em down to th' sea."

" Th' most we can expect," said Jack, " is to see our lads back. Then we can hand 'em o'er to 'em intact. Ah'll none be sorry."

" Nor me," said Joe. " They're gettin' us down."

" Hearken 'em wi' their chicken music," said Sam. " They'n browt a bit o' sunshine wi' 'em."

" It's time we were takkin' 'em whoam," said Joe. " If we don't want to get in a row."

" Come on now," said Sam. " It's gettin' bed time."

" Aye," said Bill. " Billy Winker's comin'."

" No tha can't stop another minute," said Jack. " Owt to put bed-time off. Pick that doll up."

" By gow! " said Joe. " Me legs are as stiff as a poker."

" How long does it tak' to come fro Burma? " said Jack.

" Is there nowheer else on earth nobbut Burma? " said Sam. " We han lads away as well as thee."

" No," said Jack. " Ah'm not carryin thee. It tak's me all me time to carry mesel'. Tha'll ha' to walk."

Viola Meynell

THE SICK CHILD

"TO-MORROW he will be better." Too long
   Dumb lips, pitiful eyes, too long to leave!
O for a dawn to-night!—for a bird's song,
A dew, a freshness, a new sun at eve!
A bright East for your sake, a disarray
Of all the heavens to bring your break of day!

ARAB MARE AND FOAL

Agnes Miller Parker

S. L. Bensusan

THE LONG JOURNEY

"THAT'S a handsome house, mind ye," Mr. Pottle would admit to his very few intimates, " but it want a wife an' a family same as it used to have; it ain't friendly to me. Telly f'r why. That'll wanter feel full an' it knows I can't fill it. A house got its Natur same as it was a pig or a cow, an' you can't go agin Natur."

The big off-hand farm known as Dyke Wick or Dykes, stretches to the sea wall; the workers, or most of them, live in a range of cottages sheltered from the east by the ample steading. The ' Looker ', as the foreman is called, lives in a small part of the farm house that once housed prosperous arable farmers and their large families. To-day the owner-farmer of Dykes is to be found up street some six miles away and only drives down once or twice a week to direct the Looker's acts of husbandry. He felt that there could be no purpose in preserving the outstanding feature of a period house, so he plastered the draughty inglenook fireplaces, limewashed the beamed ceilings, covered the panelled walls of the living-room with a gay paper—yellow geraniums on a blue ground—and was satisfied that he had shown himself a good and considerate landlord. " I reckon I've fixed you up smart," he said, when the work was completed and all the interior beauty of Dykes had been obliterated.

" I'll allow it's same as a good owd-fashioned place onderneath by the good rights, but I don't favour it none th' more f'r that," Saul Pottle the Looker may tell you if he knows you well enough to enter into conversation, but he is scant of speech. A lonely soul that Master Pottle; he holds it is wrong to be on too friendly terms with the staff, lest they should ' same as take advantage ', and there is nobody else within easy reach except Joe Stint, old age pensioner of Sandy Point, another widow man.

Sandy Point gives its name to a small cottage looking out over the estuary, and catching a far glimpse of Maychester too. It is another period piece, this corner of marshland is full of them, built on a frame of oak with two inglenooks and some Jacobean panelling in the living-room. Saul Pottle finds the cottage homely and attractive. It helps Joe Stint to draw him from Dykes when he has a little free time which comes to him chiefly in the dead of the year.

The Master Stint used to be familiar figure in the Street. He came up from the marshes first as a boy with his mother, then as a young man with his sweetheart, sometimes in middle age with his wife or their children, then in old age as what we call a widow man left quite alone in the world. As a result of a life of hard work and a small legacy he owns his cottage and possesses what he calls his ' Savin's Bank '. But his last journey upstreet is behind him; he admitted as much to Saul Pottle, who looked troubled and urged him ' not to talk so '. When you have but one neighbour it is hard to lose him.

*   *   *

" You don't see Master Stint hereabouts nowadays," Mrs. Timm remarked to Mrs. Martha Ram, " folk do say he's right down porely."

" I doubt you on't see him no more till he come up in his box to lay there," replied Mrs. Martha Ram, jerking her elbow towards the churchyard; " he's most tore out, pore owd chap."

" Even then we on't same as see him, by the good rights," was Mrs. Timm's shrewd yet cheerful comment. " But there, we don't none of us git younger, Martha."

" That's a true word," agreed Mrs. Ram, " I git older every

year of me life an' there's no denyin' of it. That ain't no use purtendin' in this world. Th' years keep all on comin' an' gooin', they on't stop, nit f'r nobody."

*　　　*　　　*

Several people enquired about that Master Stint, though no more reticent man ever dwelt at the back of beyond. But Maychester remembers Mary his wife who went through her brief life facing every hardship with a smile; it remembers the children " twinses each o' th' both on 'em." The girl went to the place called Austryliar and has never written, the boy went with a trawler to fish off the Dogger Bank in a November gale and also stayed away. That Master Stint never cared to talk to nobody about these happenings; they were his private grief.

Nobody save Saul Pottle, Mrs. Dynes from the cottages and Dr. Guiver called at Sandy Point where that Master Stint was laid aside. In addition to the four-roomed house that was his pride so long as he had any, there is a garden that he kept productive, and several hives of bees that survived by reason of the sanfoin, wild white clover and bulbs grown between the sea wall and Maychester. Saul Pottle tended the garden and took honey for his friend; he did so at odd hours and, for choice, when his men were on the far side of the land. He brought a pint of milk to the cottage every day, for he was entitled to a quart, and half that allowance sufficed him. If time permitted he would sit for a few minutes in one of the inglenook seats even in the busy season. It was Master Pottle who sent an ill-spelt note to Dr. Guiver asking him to call, and ' owd Guiver ' spent half an hour or more with Master Stint asking forever of questions and expressing, in reply to the only one that his patient put forward, the firm conviction that Nellie who went out furrin would probably be writing very shortly now.

"What do ye make of him, Doctor, beggin' y'r pardon?" That Master Pottle was in his garden, he had been walking anxiously up and down.

Dr. Guiver shook his head. "The machine begins to run down at his time of life, Pottle," he replied.

"I believe if that gel o' his come back," declared Mr. Pottle, "he'd peck up wunnerful."

"He might," agreed Dr. Guiver, "but not for long I fear. Any shock would kill him. The Bible tells us you can't put new wine in old bottles. Will to live is a great force; I fear he has very little of that. He doesn't need medicine, and he doesn't want much food and he isn't in any pain. Mrs. Dynes tells me you are very good to the old fellow."

"She dedn't wanter talk so," cried Pottle flushing violently and very annoyed with Mrs. Dynes. "She don't wanter talk what don't concern her. A interferin' dollops, Susan Dynes, an' no mistake. If th' dear Lord bin an' made wimmen without tongues that'd ha' bin better f'r them an' better f'r us. I never bin an' said I was good to him ne yet to nobody."

*　　　*　　　*

Mr. Stint's seat in the porch, very reluctantly abandoned, was vacant now. He had retired to one of the inglenooks in the living-room, and talked not only with absent Nellie but with his wife, calling her by name, to the great concern of Mrs. Dynes who declared roundly that a Christian didn't wanter behave so, 'skeerin' a woman outer her siven senses.' When Mr. Pottle called, that Master Stint frequently asked if Bob and Nellie would be coming back soon, thereby disconcerting Mr. Pottle, whose further anxiety lay in the fact that his friend was growing feebler week by week. The Looker could see the time when he would be left alone on the off-hand farm without a friend and when the cottage he liked so well might pass to a stranger.

"You ain't got a letter from Austryliar in Maychester by any chance, f'r owd Joe Stint, I mean," he asked the postmaster when he went up street. Mr. Ridger shook his head.

"I ain't see a letter to Sandy Point this fower year, what I kin remember," he replied with quick understanding, "an' las' time one come, pos'man should say he gotter read it to him. Telly f'r why: nobody never larnt him. Folk don't get letters from Austryliar here what I know on, except Bob Stuttle up street. He got a cousin writes him whiles, three or fower times a year I reckon."

"D'ye think he'd give me th' loan of one of his onvelopes if I took care on't?" enquired Mr. Pottle.

"There ain't no harm in astin'," replied Mr. Ridger cautiously. "Nex' one he git I'll tell postman to ask, time he give it him."

On the following Saturday afternoon Mr. Pottle visited the village library and made Australia's acquaintance under guidance of the school-mistress. Hitherto it had only been a name to him and he took notes with very great difficulty, for he is not what he would call 'same as a scholar', indeed he finds the plough easier to handle than the pen.

"The onvelope ain't no use to me," said Mr. Stuttle to the postman a few weeks later; "you kin take it an' give it to Master Ridger. There, wait a minit an' I'll open it careful f'r ye, over th' kittle. Me wife's gone up street, she won't wanter know what I'm a doin' on," he added, "so she on't be able to put me wrong about it."

*　　　*　　　*

"I brought it up meself," cried Mr. Pottle in triumphant tones, just two days later.

"Brought what, Saul?" enquired Mr. Stint feebly; he sat huddled over a small fire in the kitchen living-room.

"A letter from Austryliar," said Mr. Pottle. "That bin an' come at last."

Mr. Stint made a sudden grab and snatched the envelope.

"That'll be me Nellie," he cried and stared at the paper with eyes that could not help him.

"Happen you'd like I should read it to ye," suggested Mr. Pottle; but Mr. Stint shook his head.

"I count Nellie ouldn't like that," he replied, "that'll be privit like, she ouln't want anybody but me should see it."

"I'l never breathe a word to a livin' sowl," protested Mr. Pottle, but Mr. Stint still hesitated.

"She may be comin' home," urged Mr. Pottle desperately, for the envelope held his first and last essay and must not be lost if he could save it. "She may want you to meet a trine at Market Waldron. I could take ye up in one o' th' farm carts to carry her an' the things. Master allus sez I kin borry a horse an' cart, time I want it, an' it ain't once in a blue moon I do."

"That'd be wunnerful genteel o' ye, Saul," cried Mr. Stint, now deeply moved to acquiescence. "Happen you'd best read what she sez an' tell me time o' her trine, but you don't wanter tell her I let ye see it. That might aggravate her, though she knows I ain't no scholar."

Mr. Pottle opened the envelope, took out a letter and read as follows :

My dere dad I take up my pen to rite these few lines hopin' you are quite well as t.g. it leaves as joly—me dere dad i bin goin' to rite all these yeres but i bin so busy— austryliars a big place that got the pacific ocean on th' right han' side an' the indian on the left—my dere dad it got a lot of places without rine, an' shep an' lots of orstriches an' deserts an' sech an' we grow forever of corn—my dere dad there ain't a many folk here bein' its sech a large place it want a lot o' folk to fill it an' there ain't all that many an' the capital bin called melbourne but theres forever of other places sech as sidny an' brisbane—my dere dad i'll be comin' over soon along of me husban' an' the fower children what i've had sin' i come out here, two of both, an' i'll rite an'

tell you what time the trine git to the station so you can
come up an' help me with me box—me dere dad i'm going
to git reddy now so i will conclude with love an' kisses.

"That's a beautiful letter to my thinkin'," said Mr. Stint
joyfully. "Bin busy, else she'd ha' written, that's natural
enough; she allus kep' a doin' did my Nellie. That mus' be a
wunnerful big place along o' all them naimes. Gimme me
letter back, Saul, or happen you ouldn't mind readin' it to me
agen. She must ha' larned a lot time she bin out there. How
long does that take to git here from Austryliar?" he enquired,
when the second perusal came to an end.

"On'y six weeks or so," replied the Looker, "but happen
th' sea's rough she'll wait awhile. You don't wanter take
children to sea, time there's a gile," he explained, "do, that
may make 'em sick."

But Mr. Stint did not heed.

"I gotter git Bob here too," he said; "he bin out on th' owd
trawler long enough. I'd like to have each o' th' both on 'em
back. Then happen Mary'd stop, stiddy comin' in f'r a minit
or two at a time, time I'm jest gooin' to drop me eyelids."

"Yes," agreed Mr. Pottle uneasily, "that'd be a good thing
to have 'em all together like."

"You see, Saul," his friend explained very slowly, "time
you set by y'rself day arter day, you feel th' miss o' th' folk
you had about ye." Mr. Pottle nodded agreement.

"I've had Mary here o' late," the old man went on, "but I
can't git her to stay. She'll come an' set opposite me mos'
every evenin', she don't say nawthen to me but jest looks in f'r
company, like; she never talked much dedn't Mary. But she
ain't altered any in all these years, so I suppose Bob an' Nellie
ain't either. But I can't get me Bob here ne yet me Nellie.
That's too far f'r 'em to come, I doubt."

"Nowadays," ventured his friend, "folk git about an' don't
think anything to it. Rileways an' moty cars an' airyplanes

an' sech. T'ain't like it used to be time we was boys, Joe."

"None o' them things ain't goin' to do me no good, Saul," said Mr. Stint, after a pause. "I'm feelin' wunnerful shrunk, I ain't no strength in me bones. There's whiles I don't know if I'm asleep or awake, I'm here an' I'm somewheres else."

Mr. Pottle thought desperately for some appropriate reply. His friend's reaction chilled the hopes developed while he composed the letter that dealt so intimately with foreign parts.

"You'll have to git y'rself strong agen and wait f'r 'em," he said at last with an effort, "they'll come back together, that's likely." To this Mr. Stint made strange, disconcerting reply.

"They're a long way off arter all, Saul," he said, "an' there's two of 'em an' fower little uns an' on'y one o' me. Happen that'll be easier f'r me to goo to they. Mary can git about where she like seem'ly, an' if she can I oughter be able."

Two days passed. Mr. Pottle sat by the bedside and Dr. Guiver called for a few minutes and then Mr. Stint set out on his long journey. Sorrowful Mr. Pottle could but take the letter from cold limp fingers that had never relinquished it.

John Brophy

THE PRODIGAL CALF

THIS happened in Italy in the mountains.

One night a small squad of infantrymen was ordered to move forward and establish a post just behind the crest of a tiny hill between two other hills, themselves only the lower buttresses of a hill so big that it was often referred to as " the mountain ". The Germans held part of " the mountain ": a few days before they had held all of it. The squad was led by Corporal Basham, and when he set off he had five men.

The food was sufficient to last forty-eight hours. After that, if they were not relieved, the squad would have their emergency rations to fall back on.

On the way forward two of the squad were hit by a shell which burst on a rock. One man got a piece of splintered casing in his chest. The other came off more lightly, and Corporal Basham ordered him to lead the badly hit man back to an aid post. The remainder of the party were now heavily burdened with food, barbed wire, mines, and boxes of grenades and ammunition, as well as their weapons and equipment. They reached the little hill more than half an hour after scheduled time.

It was after midnight now. Corporal Basham surveyed his position and found a nick in the ground, near the top of the ridge, where he could post a man to watch forward. Then he arranged a roster for guard duties and sited the two Bren guns. It looked as though, only four in all, he and his men would get little sleep, and he was glad that his outpost duty was to last no more than forty-eight hours.

" The mountain " towered above him as he lay beside his Bren gun. It shouldered up, black and massive, against the stars. Posts, stronger than his own, were to be established on the two buttress hills, and that meant that he would be protected on both flanks. But about an hour after the Corporal had completed his arrangements, there came sudden abrupt noises, first from the right flank, then from the left : sudden spirts of golden light; muzzle flashes; pistol flares; the crimson flamings of detonated grenades; the rat-tat-tat of automatic fire, and shouts.

" Looks like they've run into Jerry out there," said Corporal Basham. He wondered if the flank posts would be established after all. If not, the situation would not be so funny. He reckoned to be pretty tough himself, and he was glad the three men with him were tough types, also. The Corporal was a professional soldier. He was not tall but very strong, and he rather liked hard work : sweat and strain kept his self-respect in good condition. Of the other three, Gideon and Caleb were both townsmen, but neither of them soft-handed. Caleb had worked at a flour mill, on the hoists, before he joined the army, and Gideon's job was any sort of manual labour that came his way. He had worked with a shovel at coal depots, with a pneumatic drill at road-mending. And a dozen other jobs as well. The fourth man, Amos, was the only one who came from the country. He had worked on the same farm all his life, since he was a small boy, anyhow. Corporal Basham decided it would not have been easy to pick three likelier lads for the job in hand. They were tough, all right.

He moved up to where Gideon and Caleb were lying side by side, He found them cursing each other.

" What's up? " he whispered. " And keep quiet, the pair of you."

" Look at this, Corp."

A small cylindrical ration can was thrust into his free hand.

" What's the matter with it? "

" It's milk," Gideon whispered back.

" Well? What about it? "

" They're all milk. Caleb, the b.f., he must have picked up the wrong sack at the stores."

" I tell you it was the Q.M.'s fault," Caleb protested. " Anyhow, how could I tell the difference in the dark? "

" You ought to have made sure. You see what it is, Corp. We got biscuits and we got chocolate—fancy stuff. But no meat. No meat at all. Only about ten times as much milk as we want."

" It wasn't my fault," Caleb maintained.

" It was an' all."

" Shut up, both of you!" said the Corporal. " O.K. We've got milk instead of meat. Well, it might have been worse. We just got to live on milk, that's all. It's nourishing, anyhow."

*   *   *

" Did you hear a sound just now? " Caleb asked the Corporal.

" Lots."

" I don't mean that. I mean a funny sound. Like someone in pain. Or someone having a nightmare."

" Where did it come from? "

" Couldn't tell. Listen! There it is again. It's not far away either."

The sound was low, not strong, but strangely hollow and reverberant.

" You're right," Corporal Basham whispered. " It's not far away. But where? Keep your eyes skinned, both of you. I'm going back to warn Amos."

This time he crawled over the rocks and the muddy grass, and when he came up beside Amos, before he could ask a question, Amos said, in his slow, deliberate way. " Don't worry about that noise, Corp. I'll tell you what it is. It's a cow. That's all."

" Sure? "

"Dead sure. Funny thing, though, it's behind us. It might be a calf. Yes, it'll be a calf. Not a big one either."

"I'm going to have a look," said the Corporal.

Within ten minutes he brought them news. Amos had guessed right. The noises were made by a calf. The Corporal said he found it shut into a small enclosure of stone walls, which Amos said was probably a pen used when sheep were dipped. There was a brook running beside it. The calf was quite small, so far as the Corporal could see. The stone pen had been built in a hollow, with big boulders to protect it. There was no need now for them to dig a slit trench before daylight: all except the look-out man could go into the pen when daylight came.

"That calf," said the Corporal, "It's head's not up to my waist."

"Big enough," Caleb decided. "Now who says we've got no meat? And not bully either. Who's for a nice bit of fresh veal?"

They joked about the feasts they were going to have, and they argued about which parts of the meat they would roast and which they would boil.

"If the other lads knew what a bit of luck we're having," said Gideon, "they'd be volunteering by the dozen to come up here for dinner to-morrow."

"That's right," said Gideon. "You don't want to cook meat as soon as it's killed. It ought to hang a bit."

Soon after dawn, which came late, hindered by a heavy rainfall, the Corporal realized that the squad's position in the outpost was not so secure as it was designed to be. The platoons which had gone forward on the flanks to occupy the buttress hills in front had not been able to get there or, at any rate, to stay there. The Germans were in occupation. Gideon, moving clumsily, showed his head for a second or two over the sky-line, and at once bullets began to swish over and around the squad, some of them making silvery rapid arcs in the morning light as they ricochetted off rocks.

" Blast you, Gideon!" said the Corporal. " Now they know we're here."

But the Germans were not comfortable either. Their posts came under counter fire from British machine-guns and light artillery sited in the rear.

" Well," said the Corporal. " Jerry isn't going to come and disturb us here. Not with that field of fire to cross. We'll get by. It might be worse."

" I'm hungry," Gideon complained. " A man wants meat. Biscuits and milk!"

" Well, what about that calf? "

Caleb said there was a hole in the ground where they could build a fire and do some cooking, and if one man stood by to beat the smoke away by flapping a coat, it wouldn't be detected on a drizzling, grey day. He was anxious to make amends for mistaking tins of milk for tins of preserved meat.

They left Gideon on guard and went back down the slope to look at the hole. Corporal Basham admitted that cooking was possible. He knew, too, that hot food on a day like this would make a lot of difference to the spirit of his men. So he told Amos to start a small fire and boil some water to make tea. Then, with Caleb, he went to look at the calf in the stone wall pen. It was making plenty of noise now.

In daylight it seemed very small. Its coat was bedraggled with rain and mud. They could see its throat pulsating as it lowed at them.

" You know," said Caleb, " it'd look real nice, cleaned up a bit. Them reddish-brown patches on the white."

" Don't talk sissy," said the Corporal. " What have you got to kill it with? Bayonet or your knife? "

" Kill it? Me? I wouldn't know how to begin. Tell you what, I'll slip back and help Amos brew up."

The calf lowed again. It walked across to where they peered at it through a hole in the stone wall. Its eyes glistened, big and brown and lustrous, through the downpouring rain.

"And some people call themselves soldiers!"

"I'm not scared o' Jerry, Corporal. And anyhow, why don't you kill it yourself? It'd only need a short burst with your Sten gun."

"Mustn't waste ammunition," said Corporal Basham. "Tell you what, we'll let Gideon do the job."

"That's right. Gideon, he's the one. I remember he told me he used to work in a tannery once. It wouldn't mean anything to him."

"All right," the Corporal decided. "You go and relieve him on guard. Tell him to report here at once."

Gideon came back very cocky. Even though he had to crawl part of the way, and stoop when he was not crawling, he contrived to move with a swagger.

"Fancy Caleb turning soft like that," he said. "Don't you worry, though, Corp. I'll see to this."

He unfastened the wicker gate and let himself into the pen. The calf came stumbling up to him at once. He put out his hand and it nuzzled its lips against his palm.

Gideon looked up.

"It's no good," he complained. "I couldn't do it. I haven't the heart. I'd never sleep quiet again."

The Corporal was almost beaten by this time. He had to remind himself that it was his duty to secure the best available provisions for his men in order to maintain maximum efficiency.

"It'll have to be Amos, then," he declared.

"We ought to have thought of Amos first of all," said Gideon. "He's a farmer's boy. It won't mean anything to him."

But Amos, when he was fetched to the pen, protested that he was no butcher. And as soon as he set eyes on the calf, he turned indignantly to the other two, completely disregarding the respect due to Corporal Basham's rank.

"You're a fine couple. Can't you see the poor beast's half-starved? Jerry drove away the cow, I expect, and forgot this poor little beggar. Just like Jerry!"

" Do you mean to say it's still taking milk? "

" Yes, and will be for months yet. Only I'll bet it's not had a feed for a couple of days. It wants its mother. It's weak, poor little blighter. It can hardly stand up. Haven't you got eyes in your heads? "

The Corporal felt as conscience-stricken as Gideon, till he had an idea.

" Of course," he said, " We've got lashings of milk."

They made a run for the fire then, and opened a can of the condensed milk and mixed it with warm water in a mess tin. They fed the calf before they thought of feeding themselves. Amos dipped his fingers in the milk, and the calf sucked them. Then it began to lap from the mess tin, at first doubtfully and slowly, then fast.

As things turned out they had to stay quite a time in that outpost before the rest of the battalion worked forward on the flanks, and they could be relieved. They had to beat off several small attacks, too, and more than once they were shelled. But they all survived, including the calf.

When the squad at last marched out to rest, they were dirty and tired, dropping with sleep. They had lived for five days on two day's rations minus the essential meat, plus one day's emergency rations. Less that that, for most of the milk had gone to the calf. In effect, they had starved for the last forty-eight hours. Only the calf looked better for the experience. Its flanks were plumped out with tin after tin of milk, and the lowing noises it made were no longer plaintive, but full of the joy of life.

The squad was very proud of its acquisition. Next morning it discussed procedures for having the calf adopted as the regimental pet. But by afternoon an Italian farmer had visited the camp and claimed the calf as his property. After he had seen the interpreter and the interpreter had seen the adjutant, and several forms had been signed in triplicate, the farmer led the calf away in triumph.

"Well," said Corporal Basham, "that's that."

"It's a bleedin' shame. We ought to have been allowed to keep it," Caleb declared. "It don't seem a bit fair somehow."

Gideon also was not satisfied. "I miss the little blighter," he said. "Tell you what, when the war's over, I'm coming back here somehow. Ship on a boat as a deckhand, or something. And I'm going to look for that farmer, and tell him the least he can do is give me a glass of milk. Free. For nix. And it's got to be milk from our calf. It'll be a fine cow by then, see."

Amos laughed.

"You'll get no milk."

"I will. Bet you I will. The old farmer chap won't grudge it me, when I tell him I saved his cow from certain death when it was a bit of a calf, hardly up to my waist."

"You townies," said Amos. "You don't notice nothing. That was a bull calf."

BUILDING THE RICK

Clifford Webb

R. H. Chadwick

IN AND OUT

THE turnstile clicked and we were in. In for what? Half-a-crown, in spot cash—a shilling for myself and ninepence each for the junior bathers. But otherwise it remained to be seen.

Dogs, whether as bathers or spectators, were refused admission. "You'd better cut home now, Walker," said Garry, over the turnstile, to the embodiment of faithfulness, who was getting rather in the way of the queue. "He'll have quite a trot," he added, cheerfully, thinking of the two miles home.

Under its mosques and minarets, a dozen years ago the latest thing in natatory architecture though now looking a trifle more than off-white, were about a thousand bathers in the shallows of the pool. Ankle-deep, knee-deep, up to their waists, they looked in this setting like those who wash in holy Ganges. There were so many of them.

"We shall never get in!" cried Garry, aghast.

"You'll never get in there," said Miranda, gleefully, pointing towards where gentlemen were to change from their clothes to their costumes, and now formed a vast queue against the skyline. "But I'm a lady," she shouted, joyously, bounding off towards her own place, which looked less thronged.

"Here!" I cried. If we parted like this we might never meet again.

Miranda brought to heel, I charged her solemnly. Changed, she was to sit at the foot of the cascade, nor stir from there on any pretext, and abide our coming whether that were in an hour's time or next Christmas. Nor could she have an ice.

Miranda, making the motions of diving throughout these instructions, heard clearly. "Woosh!" she cried, pretending to cleave the water in a dive quite beyond her ten years' nerve.

Garry and I lined up with Polish airmen, British airmen, British infantry, G.I. Joes, youths loutish and debonair, and plain, stubby, middle-aged citizens like myself. Also with Walker.

I communicated this discovery to Garry in an undertone. "I know," he whispered back, fiercely. "There's a place in the railings behind the rose bushes. I could kick his ribs in!" It was not as if he was ours. But he was an acquaintance very difficult to slight. He excited attention, too. "Cut smelling, dawg," said a Yank.

It was the height of the heat-wave and the sun smote us unbearably. I wondered if glaring white concrete was one of our untried secret weapons. Walker lay down, panting.

"I shall be glad to get in," I observed, genially, to a curious old nut-brown fellow in white "ducks" and singlet, who seemed to have lost his place in the queue, but who, I afterwards found, was a swimming-pool attendant.

"You'll take your place like the others," he replied, sharply.

Walker was baulked at the inner turnstile where they took the bathers' tickets, and the last I saw of him at this stage was his flight before the angry old attendant whose tattoo-marks—hearts pierced by Cupid's arrows—did not mean that he loved dogs, too.

Inside, we were separated. I had cubicle 13; Garry, 812. I left cubicle 13 after one of the strangest tussles in my experience —with my swim-suit. Since my last dip it had shrunk inconceivably, or I had fattened beyond my worst fears. Probably both. I might have been sewn up in calico for dispatch to foreign parts, so tight I was. I could hardly move. Should I be able to swim in the thing?

Out in the bathers' enclosure Garry, who is a fairly well-made boy of thirteen, awaited me. When I saw him I laughed like Little Audrey. Whatever I was in his, in my swim-suit he was an object to scare crows—all folds and drapery.

"But I couldn't find you in all that scrum!" he howled. "Change! Oh, we can't now, uncle! Miranda'll be stiff with waiting."

But Miranda wasn't stiff at all. As we set out for the rendezvous, an observed couple, through hundreds of basking bathers, fair, freckled and hirsute, ranging from near-Godivas to those who slept in horn-rimmed spectacles, we met her running. Miranda was in apparent flight from a sort of Caliban, a low-bred, mis-shapen, but powerful lad, who, a yard behind her, fell upon another fleet-footed youth and heaved him bodily into six feet of water. Miranda was shouting "Uncle! uncle!" after a man who didn't know her. Beyond all this a great commotion was taking place, a hue-and-cry after Walker, in which I observed our old friend in "ducks" and singlet was taking part.

But there were nearer matters. "Hi-di-ho! Ollerenshaw," cried Garry, hailing Caliban by this unexpected name.

What particular subtlety, perhaps malicious, underlay this informal greeting I do not know, but he instantly turned on Garry and sent him flying, like his first victim, into deep water. Walker, coming our way, and eluding all attempts at capture, went in after him. Could Garry swim? I did not really know. It proved he could, but no mandarin in his robes could have had more difficulty breasting the Yangtse than had Garry in my bathing-suit in reaching the side.

All around people rose to their feet. Strong swimmers plunged to Garry's rescue. I hung from the step-ladder with outstretched hand. Miranda lost her head, crying: "Don't drown, Garry! Please don't drown!" From a row behind I gathered that Caliban was in informal custody.

As I pulled Garry, panting, up the ladder, with the faithful Walker making the most piteous attempts to follow, a sudden rending of fabric told me the worst had happened. A vast press of bathers nearly shoved us in again. The tattooed attendant elbowed his way through.

"Trying to sink yourself, my lad, in your—dressing-gown," he said to Garry. "And you, sir," he reproved me; "you'd better skip back and change, sharp. Bathing in your little brother's things!"

Garry dried and dressed, I and Miranda just dressed, we left the bathing pool. Near the exit we were joined by Walker, inconceivably still at large. Garry made a wet armful of him. Then the turnstile clicked and we were out.

Music by ROGER QUILTER

Words by RODNEY BENNETT

★

THERE was no cradle for Jesus
    When he was small,
Only a rough wooden manger
    In a poor stall;
Yet the baby who lay there so lowly
    Was king of us all.

There was no lamp in the stable
    That winter night,
Only a shepherd's dim lantern
    Gave fitful light;
Yet the star that burned over the rooftree
    Made all heaven bright.

No man made music for Jesus,
    Songs they made none;
Only heaven's angels were praising
    Father and Son
In a song that will ring down the ages
    Till ages are done.

We sing the glory of Jesus
    As they sang then.
Soon may the whole earth re-echo
    That song again :
Praise and glory to God in the highest,
    Good will toward men.

The Cradle in Bethlehem

Words by :
RODNEY BENNETT

Music by :
ROGER QUILTER

There was no cra-dle for Je-sus When he was small, On-ly a rough wood-en man-ger . . In a poor stall: . . Yet the ba-by who lay there so

low-ly   Was King of us all. . .

There was no lamp in the sta - ble . . That   win-ter   night, . .

On-ly a shepherd's dim lan-tern . . gave   fit - ful   light, . . Yet the

star that burn'd o-ver the   roof-tree . . Made all Heaven   bright. . .

Edmund Blunden

VOICES I HEARD

"WHO are you afraid of?" "Spider Dick."
    "What's he? "What's he? Maybe Old Nick."
"But what does he do?" "Odd jobs by day,
And odder ones at night he may.
He's got such eyes they pierce you through
    He sings some rhyme in a language of his own.
I'll wait for someone going my way too
    For the floods are highering and the branches groan."

"Where are you off?" "To Fenton Folly."
"That's a day's outing." "So says my dolly."
"And what provisions?" "This dolly doesn't eat;
Or else she can live on rabbit's meat.
But we have a jam puff each and cake,
    Six or seven home-mades, and two big pies,
So we'll sit for lunch by the side of the lake
    For the sun's getting warm and the cuckoo flies."

"What a grand blue frock." "It's for Flower-Show Day,
The world's best Galloping Steeds they say,
And in the marquee there is always a pool
Of red water-lilies, right beautiful,
And I can't tell you all, but there's prizes and tea—
    We children have one small tent for our work,
I've stitched and I've sewn just as neat as can be;
    But Bella always wins, and she's a young Turk."

" So, another new book!" " I am just at the end,
And I don't think the Club has more Jules Verne to lend,
But Father's been deep in ' The War in the Air ',
It's under the cushion on the wicker chair,
And he says it's all true, we shall see it quite soon,
  And Mother seemed frightened, you know how she looks,
And when she saw *this*, ' From the Earth to the Moon ',
  She told me to keep off the nonsense in books."

Frank Swinnerton

A BEQUEST

THERE were only two people in the first-class railway carriage nearest to the engine; and Deborah was one of them. *He* had pushed a children's paper of some kind into her black-gloved hands, and was now hidden behind a big newspaper of his own. He wanted nothing to do with her. He showed as much by his sharp way of speaking—"Hurry up!" "What?" "Got all you need?" He didn't wait for answers. But in any case she did not know what to answer. She bit her lip very hard. Her heart had crept right down into her tummy, where it stuck like a ball of cold water. If it ever came up again, she knew she would cry.

But Mrs. Vanbrugh had whispered—they were her last words: "Whatever you do, don't cry. *He hates it.* Try and make a good impression!"

Mrs. Vanbrugh's cold cheek, cold lips. . . . What was "a good impression?" She hadn't made it. Deborah's tears, being withheld, gathered behind her eyes. "I mustn't cry! I mustn't!" Her nose was smarting dreadfully. She blew her nose in a sort of whisper—chee, chee, chee. . . . And the big newspaper opposite gave an angry jerk. *He* had heard, and thought she was crying. She wasn't. She *wouldn't* cry.

She pressed back against the cushion, and looked out of the window. The train was running not far from a wide road, on which a car flew along. The car was black. It was like an express ant. You could not see its wheels turning, any more than you could see an ant's legs. . . .

"I'm . . . sorry, old girl. . . ." It was Mummy's drawly,

heavy voice of sickness that came into her ears from the past. " I'm afraid I'm . . . going to leave you alone. I'm so . . . *sorry*."

Deborah almost screamed. She was choking. Mummy's voice was so close that she did not dare to shut her eyes. If she shut them she would see Mummy as she had been on that terrible afternoon. She had shrieked then : " Mrs. Vanbrugh! Mrs. Vanbrugh! Come quick! Mummy's dead!" She had known. Mummy had gone all quiet and white and *small*.

Mrs. Vanbrugh had dragged her away. She'd smacked her hands; then her face. " All this fuss! I can't bring her back! A big girl of seven, screaming!"

Mrs. Vanbrugh didn't understand. She didn't know how it felt to be so much afraid. Mummy had known. Mummy always knew just how you felt. She saw just what *you* saw, and laughed as much as you did. That was why their games were such fun. But their games were over. He, a stranger, behind his paper . . . so stern . . . " Hurry up!" " What? " " Got all you need? " " Whatever you do, don't cry!"

" I can't bear it!" She was crying. Streams of warmth ran down her cheeks and trickled under her chin. Her hanky was soaked. Mummy would have hugged her, made her better. " That better, my darling? " Even when she was ill, dying, Mummy had let Deborah hold her hand and rest cheek to cheek in comforting love. " When I'm better, when I'm up again, we'll . . . won't it be fun!" Oh, Mummy, Mummy!

She mustn't cry like this. The dye was coming off her gloves on to her hanky, perhaps on to her face. She took off the gloves; but it was too late. The blackened hanky had made great streaks there; she could see them when she looked down. *He* would see. He would be angry. " Don't make him angry," Mrs. Vanbrugh had said. " I can tell he's bad-tempered." He *was* seeing. He *was* angry.

" Good heavens, child! *This* won't do!"

The crackling paper had been thrown down. He was glaring at her. He was going to hit her. . . .

" Your face is smeared with black. Those wretched cheap gloves! What the woman——. Can you wash yourself? In the train lavatory? Here, wait a bit!" He had stood up, opened the door to the corridor, and was waiting for her. " Come on!"

What was he going to do? Deborah seemed not to be able to move. She was paralysed. At last she took his impatient hand, and they walked along the narrow, reeling passage, to a little lavatory in the corner. He stood back, holding the door wide open.

" *Look* at yourself!"

She saw a frightened little white face, red-nosed and red-eyed, with streaks of black all over it. A black hat, a black coat; long blackish hair that dangled to her shoulders. A swollen mouth, in which two big front teeth were twice as big as any of the others. She looked in vain for a sponge, or a flannel; and stood dumbly without doing anything at all. She knew he must be angry with her. Was he always angry? She was as small as an insect. She wished she could die, or hide. She was awfully afraid.

Then that sharp voice:

" What is it now? " It became kinder: " Oh, something to do it with. That's a problem!" He had produced a clean handkerchief. He was soaking it. He was washing her face! He was quite gentle. It was lovely when he brought the hanky across her forehead. She would have liked him to go on doing that; but he didn't. " There! That's enough! You can dry yourself, can't you? "

They went back to the carriage, and sat down again. Deborah felt much better. He said:

" I shouldn't cry any more. You're lonely, I expect. I didn't want to leave you with that woman——Mrs. Vanbrugh. Didn't like her. Did you? "

" N-not very much," stuttered Deborah.

" Hm," he grunted. " She thought I'd leave you there. Bad enough with me; worse with her."

Deborah did not know what to do or say. She had not been fond of Mrs. Vanbrugh. Mrs. Vanbrugh could hurt you. She had hard, bony hands—very cold. But *he*. . . . He was staring. He had frightening grey eyes that didn't smile.

" You go to school, don't you? "

" Yes."

" That's *something*. I'll hang this hanky up to dry. See? " It fell down from the rack, and Deborah—because she could not help herself—giggled. He hung the hanky up again, and pegged it with a spectacle case and a tobacco pouch. It was clever of him. " You realise I'm your uncle, don't you. . . . Your father's brother. You don't remember him. No, you never saw him."

" I saw his picture."

" About as like him as a pea's like a walrus! "

" Mummy liked it."

" Hm."

Did *he* not love Mummy? Mummy had never said anything about *him*. It was always ' Your Daddy.' Deborah had never heard of *him*. Only somebody called Ricky. She and Auntie Addie used to talk of Ricky this, and Ricky that. Not *him*. He was a stranger. Mrs. Vanbrugh had said : " *Very* premtry. Deaf, too, I should think. Well, I've done *my* best." . . .

After a time she looked out of the window again. The train was going much faster. Places were simply swooshing past. He gave a frightening plunge, and jerked his head to see what was going on outside.

" Ah! " he said. " That's St. Albans. Twenty minutes more."

After twice trying to speak, without being able to make any sound, Deborah managed to get out :

" Mummy had a friend in St. Albans."

" Mm? Yes, I know her. She's in America. Adela Sims."

" Auntie Addie."

" No relation really. You liked her, did you? "

" Ooh, yes!" Deborah felt happy for the first time. " She's lovely."

" Hm," he said.

Soon there came tunnels—long, long tunnels. He looked different—more frightening still—by artificial light. His eyes went quite black and very stern. They made Deborah's heart beat fast with the fear that she would be clumsy, and he would be angry with her. He was taking her to his house in London— something called a flat—where there would be no escape. Mrs. Vanbrugh had said : " Not my idea of the way to bring up a child—all smoke and whisky. He's mad. He ought to *pay* someone to look after you."

Did Mrs. Vanbrugh mean herself ? But Mrs. Vanbrugh wasn't kind. She had slapped Deborah. Mrs. Vanbrugh liked slapping. " You want a strong hand; that what *you* want." Mrs. Vanbrugh clenched her teeth when she shook you. . . .

Something in the memory of Mrs. Vanbrugh made Deborah shiver. What *was* going to happen to her? She was most awfully worried. She felt sick. If she *were* sick he'd be furious. . . .

" Here we are," he said. The train was slowing. They were out of the tunnels, and jig-jogging over the points. There were porters and taxi-cabs just a little way away. Was this London? He took the half-dry hanky from the rack, folded it, and put it in a pocket.

" Oh, your *pouch*!" cried Deborah. He had left it, forgotten, in the rack.

" Thanks."

She had felt proud of helping him, and was crushed when he took no notice of her cleverness. He didn't think she was clever; she couldn't tell him. She could have told Mummy. " Wasn't I clever, Mummy!" But Mummy would have known. Mummy would have said : " Clever, thoughtful girl!" All *he* said was " Thanks." . . .

Then they were in the crowd on the platform, and Deborah,

I

bewildered by the noise, trotted behind that long, striding figure, which carried their two leather cases as if they had been paper bags of cakes. "Hurry up. I want to bag a taxi."

"Oh wait! *Please* wait! I'm only a *little* girl!" Mummy would have waited. Mummy would have held her hand, letting a porter take the bags. . . .

Her feet were like lead. Her eyes ached. She stumbled, and nearly fell; and had then to run to catch up with him again.

II

Deborah was no longer afraid of him. She knew now that he would never hit or hurt her; but at the worst would only cluck his tongue and look cross if she spilt anything or knocked anything down with her elbow. He took her hand if they went out; but as soon as they had crossed a street he would wriggle his fingers free, even if she tried to hold on to them. He saw all she did, all she wanted. He bought her sweets and cakes. She had learned to call him Uncle. She sometimes felt she could love him dearly if he would let her do so. He wouldn't. He did not love her. He never kissed her or called her "darling" or listened if she tried to tell him what she had been thinking. She was unhappy.

And then there was school. The other children were friends among themselves. She was a stranger. They had mothers and fathers. She had neither mother nor father. They were met by nurses or mothers, who said "Hullo, Deborah," and had no time to spare for lonely little girls. They soon shook her off. And Miss Wilson, her teacher, lost patience with clumsy writing and wrong sums and bad memory, and—before all the other children—called her stupid. How Deborah dreaded school! Miss Wrench, the headmistress, said she must do better. She said "You don't want to be a dunce, do you?" "No, Miss Wrench." "Then you must try harder." "I do try, Miss Wrench; I do, really!" "I shall have to speak to your uncle." "*Oh, no, Miss Wrench! No! Don't tell him! Don't! I'll try harder. Truly I will!*" Miss Wrench said to Miss Wilson : " She seems terrified of him."

It was worst at night, when Deborah was in bed. She lay listening. She had no light in the room; but a street lamp sent a big ray on to the ceiling. Buses rumbled in the main road, and sometimes a taxi or private car skirred past the flats. Otherwise it was very quiet. She thought of Mummy and her bad work at school and the need for not making any noise which would disturb *him*. Dreadful thoughts! She stuffed the corner of the sheet into her mouth, and bit it hard. But she cried herself to sleep night after night, and in the morning was too stupid to think of anything to say that would make him be interested in her. He read his paper. If she whispered, he looked at her and seemed bored. " Yes, hurry on with your breakfast." " Do you think we could go to Kensington Gardens on Saturday, Uncle? " " Not this week. I must work all day." " No." " What? " " Nothing, Uncle." Then one of his stern glances.

He crackled his paper to the floor and ate his own breakfast the faster. Mrs. Pemberton, the small, tough, smooth-haired woman who got Deborah ready, and cleaned the flat, and made the beds, and prepared the meals, who went home after tea, said he worked too hard.

" You should help him," Mrs. Pemberton said. She never had a moment to spare. Never time to play with little girls. And didn't believe in it, either.

" How could I? " Deborah asked.

" Well, keep your things tidy, anyway," said Mrs. Pemberton.

" That's helping *you*."

" And keep quiet."

" I do try," said Deborah.

" I don't say it's all your own fault," Mrs. Pemberton told her. " But you should be brighter. Laugh. Sing. Like I do."

" Once when I sang," grimaced Deborah, " he asked if I'd got a toothache. He said : ' Keep quiet, there's a good girl; I *must* finish this article by six.' "

" Oh, well, it's a nuisance." Mrs. Pemberton was out of the room and swirling round with the vacuum cleaner. " *I* must finish this job while he's out."

One night Deborah could *not* go to sleep. It was at the end of the day when Miss Wrench had said she would see *him*. The fear of it had given her diarrhœa; and she now felt so weak that she could not stop crying. It was terrible to go on day after day, getting stupider and into worse fixes at school. It made her feel ill. She had no hope at all. At last, when she had said : " Mummy! Mummy! I wish I could come to you!" she had lost all power to check her sobs. They racked her body. They forced themselves from her lips. They echoed in the room. Even when she felt sure the door had opened, she could not choke them back as she had done so often before.

He was there. He hadn't shouted at her, or told her to be quiet. He was beside the bed, sitting down in the chair, sitting on her folded clothes. She could see him against the window. His hand had taken hers—hers, at least, had flown to his.

" Bad dreams? " he asked. She could not say anything. The sobs were still coming too strongly. But she gripped his cool fingers and pressed them with all her might. " No? Unhappy? Go to sleep again, there's a good girl."

" I ca-can't!" she cried in a little scream. And then, thinking that his fingers were withdrawing : " Don't go!"

" Lonely? "

" Dreadfully!"

" I'll stay. I've got a surprise for you."

" Me? " She couldn't believe it. " Not Miss Wrench? "

" What? Who's Miss Wrench? What! Here, you must tell me all about this. Miss Wilson? . . . Hm. That's it, is it. . . . Well, you go to sleep. And to-morrow you shall have your surprise. A nice one."

" A dolly? "

" Oh." He sounded surprised. " No, better than a dolly."

" N-not Mrs. Vanbrugh—" A shudder shook Deborah.

" You wouldn't like that, would you? "

" Hate it."

" Well, it's nothing nasty. For one thing, you're not going to school."

" Really? " Deborah scuffled her legs in excitement.

" So go to sleep now."

" I will. I'm very sorry I disturbed you."

" You *have* disturbed me."

" I didn't mean to." She put her lips to his hand. She felt sure he did not know that she had done so.

III

In the morning she woke up feeling as gay as a kitten. She was fresh and lively; and when she jumped out of bed and ran to the window she saw that the sun was shining. No school! Hurray! And *he'd* been so sweet last night! She couldn't remember his going. He must have held her hand until she was asleep. " Oh, I *wonder* what the surprise is!"

She washed herself carefully all over, and brushed her teeth. If she wasn't going to school, were they going out? Should she wear a frock? Yes, her *best* frock. She loved it: she'd seen it in a shop, and he'd bought it; but he'd muttered a lot under his breath. It was of yellow silk, and had the most delicious pattern of tiny flowers in a lot of other colours. If Mrs. Pemberton did her hair . . .

She was ready long before breakfast time, and put his paper on the reading stand which he ought always to use. She could hear him *whistling* in the bathroom. She'd never heard that before. It was very strange. " Perhaps *that's* the surprise? " she thought, and felt her heart sink a little.

She was waiting when he came in to breakfast, and smiled

gladly at him. And he—yes, as he passed, he touched her shoulder. But he did not notice the frock, as she had hoped he would. He should have praised her for wearing it.

"Sleep all right?" he asked.

She could only nod. They had breakfast in silence, he reading his paper, she in terror lest she should drop anything on the frock. It was a tremendous time before they were done with all the details of the flat. At last they were in the taxi.

"Is this the surprise?" Deborah asked, peeping out of the window.

"Coming," said he.

They were at a big railway station. Millions of people were racing about or getting in the way. But Deborah was not afraid. She boldly took and tightly held her uncle's hand, which she would never have done before the previous night. He did not wriggle it away. And he kept whistling under his breath—Se-se-se; se-se-see. It was awfully silly.

There was no train at the platform at first. But it began to come in, very slowly indeed; and hundreds of people waved their hands and ran towards it. Why, the train was full. It had *come* from somewhere. *He* didn't wave, or run.

"Phew!" whistled Deborah. "What a long train!"

"I'm afraid you're right," he muttered.

The train stopped. Deborah didn't know anything at all about it. Suddenly she was swept off her feet as her uncle walked quickly towards one of the carriages. A lovely lady stood in the doorway, with her eyes shining.

"Is she the——" began Deborah. Then she gave a squeal. "Auntie Addie!" and rushed straight—her legs like a grasshopper's—into the lovely lady's arms.

What was stranger still was that Auntie Addie, still holding Deborah, was giving her other hand to Uncle, and looking at him as if she were going to cry; while *he* did not take any hand but boldly put his arms round Auntie Addie and kissed her.

"He never does that to me," sighed Deborah.

"Doesn't he? That's terribly remiss. Never mind, we'll teach him to, shall we?"

Deborah was rather puzzled as she looked from one to the other of them.

"How *can* we?" she asked. She saw a look pass between them—the look grown-ups exchange. Uncle shook his head.

"Ricky, darling," said Auntie Addie. "Could you see about my luggage?"

He had hurried away, while Deborah felt her wits whirling. Ricky! Was *he* Ricky? Oh, but Mummy had *loved* him!

"I didn't know he was *Ricky*!" she exclaimed. "I've been so afraid of him."

"Afraid? Oh, you poor child! Was he shy?"

"I don't know."

"I wish I'd been there. I was in America. He sent me cables about you. He was always cabling. But he said you needed *me*. So here I am."

"Oh." Deborah felt her heart give a little twist. "You're not going to take me away from him?"

Auntie Addie laughed.

"Does that frighten you?"

"Well, I don't somehow want to——" Deborah felt very strange indeed. But Auntie Addie gave her a hug.

"It's all right. We're both going to look after you."

"Are you going to marry him?"

"That's the idea."

"And keep me with you? Oh, lovely! Perfect! And last night I wanted to die!"

SNOW ON THE RADNOR HILLS

Iain Macnab

Walter De La Mare

NOSTALGIA

IN the strange city of life
Two houses I know well:
One wherein Silence her secret keeps,
And one where Dark doth dwell.

Gable and roof they stand,
Fronting the dizzied street,
Where Vanity flaunts her gilded booths
In the noontide glare and heat.

Green-graped upon their walls
Earth's ancient hoary vine
Clusters their carven lichenous stones
With tendril serpentine.

Deafened, incensed, dismayed,
Dazed in the clamorous throng,
I thirst for the soundless fount that rills
As if from my inmost heart, and stills
Those orchards mute of song.

Homeless, I knock. In vain.
Nor yet of the hidden may tell:
Where Silence perpetual vigil keeps,
Where Dark doth dwell.

Thomas Burke

AN UNCLE OF A DAY

WHEN one is eight, monotony presses heavily on the young spirit, and when I was eight my life was largely monotony. One day was almost a replica of all others. Nothing " exciting " ever happened. There were few lovely surprises, seldom an unexpected visit, and treats were rare. We lived on the bare edge of everyday necessaries, and only by a carefully considered and monotonous way of life was it possible to achieve that tortuous labour known in small households **as** making ends meet.

But Saturdays were different. Saturday was the Day of my week, the day to which all other days pointed and led. It was not a white-stone day in the high key of Christmas, with all its coloured treasure; or of Easter, with its hot-cross buns and chocolate eggs; or the Fifth of November, with its night of golden rain. But it certainly was a day of mild carnival. For one thing, it was a holiday. For another, it was pocket-money day. And again it had a quality and colour and personality of its own—a Saturday quality, a Saturday personality, genial and expansive. It was an Uncle of a day where the other days were thin, querulous Aunts. . . .

Saturday Morning, fifty years ago. . . . And I see myself, eight years old, standing at the window of a little upstairs room in a little house in a dim by-street of a South London suburb, looking out in expectation of an arrival. Most of my

Only a few days after Mr. Burke passed the proof of this contribution we learned with regret of his death—on September 23rd, 1945. Readers will be glad to have in this delightful and authentic document of boyhood one of the last examples of his unique craft as essayist.

Saturdays followed one pattern and procedure, and the particular Saturday I recall, an autumn Saturday, was typical of all of them. Saturday meant always a halfpenny at least to spend; sometimes more. I would sometimes be given a halfpenny by the landlord or the man next door, and sometimes a jam-jar would produce another halfpenny or even a penny. On that particular Saturday I had already a halfpenny, and I had two jam-jars. They were the reason for my watching at the window.

Saturday morning brought always to our little street of little houses with gay front gardens a regular procession of picturesque vagabonds selling things, collecting things, or giving comic performances or exhibitions of agility which had neither beauty nor reason and yet created a sort of poetry of the London street. The wandering merchants who came to sell things would fill the air with those Cries that are now stilled—Cries of Coal and Milk and Old Moore's Almanac, of Salt and Logs and Nuts and Shrimps, and the local Gazette and Chairs-to-Mend and Hearth-Brooms and Knives-to-Grind—Cries that told you nothing of the wares they offered unless you knew the Eskimo language of Street Cries, and could interpret Myo-Koo as Milk, and Whu-Ho as Coals, and Gran-Hoo as Knives-to-Grind. And the performers would bring music of cornet or drum, and the collectors would ring hand-bells, so that the outdoor movement and noise alone told you that it was a Saturday Morning.

Those I looked for were not the sellers or performers but the collectors. The first of these, as punctual as the clock, brought into the street what looked like a ship dressed for regatta or review. This was a barrow piled high with stocks of paper windmills on sticks, paper flags of all nations, and coloured air-balloons. Any of those bright marvels could be had in exchange for a jam-jar. But desirable as they were they did not appeal to me. I preferred money, and I waited for the barrow of the man who gave a halfpenny for glass jam-jars and a penny for those of earthenware. That morning I had two earthenwares, and when at last he arrived, and our business was done, I sped away to the High Street with as much as twopence-halfpenny to spend. Twopence-halfpenny, or five halfpennies, or ten farthings.

On my way to the High Street I passed one or two street-performers going through their antics, but the thought of the five halfpennies or ten farthings so excluded all other interests that I did not even look at them, let alone stop. A street-organ was churning out *Her Golden Hair Was Hanging Down Her Back*, and at the corner groups of my acquaintance were engaged in various singing-rituals of pastoral name—*Wall-flowers, Jenny is a-Weeping, I sent a Letter to my Love, Mary in the Meadow*—folk survivals from the village-greens of a thousand years, to which they had descended in garbled form from the religions of lost races of the Mediterranean.

All street-games in those days had their peculiar and unaccountable seasons. At a certain time of the year peg-tops would be brought out. For a month or so they would be the vogue; then, as suddenly as they appeared, they would disappear, and their place would be taken by marbles. Then marbles would disappear, and singing-games would take their place, and then singing-games would give way to hoops. Nobody could say just when those seasons opened and closed. There was no sporting calendar in which their dates were set. Nor was there any question of one or two children in a given district bringing out tops on the first of May and setting a fashion for the rest; nor was there any mutually agreed un-written code. It was something spontaneous which moved in the blood and set thousands of children, individually, in one particular week of the year, to produce tops, and set them again simultaneously, in another week, to lay tops aside and produce marbles. It was such an instinct as moves a hundred individual apple-trees at one time to blossom, or moves a million individual swallows in the same week to make flight to the south.

Those toys and games have now disappeared not only from the streets but I believe from the playgrounds. No longer do the little suburban sweet-shops show peg-tops or marbles or five-stones or iron hoops or skipping-ropes. Conkers and cherry-stones are no longer playthings. The child of to-day knows nothing of the games described in that queer Norman Douglas book, *London Street Games*. What has taken their place? I don't know; but at that time they were part of the scene of every London suburb.

With my twopence-halfpenny firmly held I began my tour of the High Street shops at the station end, and worked my way up, lingering at each of them, drawn by the pictures made by their window-dressing to do my Saturday Morning shopping now here and now there. There was the baker's with its pyramids of many shapes and styles of bread—the cottage-loaf, the brick-loaf, the Coburg, the tin-loaf, the Vienna twist. There was the ham-and-beef shop, with its glossy ox-tongues, its brown roast chickens, its sausages in red and green and silver paper. And the massed colours of the cakes and pastries in the confectioner's window, which made it like something out of a Christmas Number. With the flip of each door, as shoppers came and went, I caught the odour peculiar to each shop—the earthiness of the greengrocer's, the clean richness of the confectioner's, the pungency of the chemist's, the solemnity of the draper's, the piquancy of the grocer's and the warm tang of the baker's. At those shops which had an outside stall, such as greengrocer and newsagent, I received a greeting. I sometimes spent two halfpennies with them, and the assistants knew me, so my progress up the street was a series of Morning Calls.

After I had toured both sides, up and down, I stood and debated what to do with my five halfpennies. I had no notion of saving part of them for Monday or Wednesday. Whatever my Saturday money, whether a halfpenny or a penny or even what it was on that rare occasion, my way was always to dash it in one Saturnalia. But the appeals were conflicting, the possibilities of choice bewildering. I decided at last on biscuits, a comic paper, sweets and something from the greengrocer's. But each choice, in its turn, offered various sub-attractions. At the big confectioner's you could get for a penny three of yesterday's pastries or two of that day's heart-cakes or one of that day's jam-puffs. At the grocer's you could get for a halfpenny a large bag of broken wafers. Of comic papers you could get for a halfpenny *Comic Cuts* or *Chips* or the *Funny Wonder*. At the greengrocer's were oranges, bananas, chestnuts and pomegranates. Small oranges were four a penny, bananas three a penny, pomegranates two a penny, and for a penny they would give you a whole capful of chestnuts. The pomegranate wasn't very satisfying or delicious in the eating, but it was a lovely word to bring out, and it was a lovely thing to hold and look at—the polished brown-gold of its rind, and its odd shape, and the gorgeous colour of its inside. I hesitated on the common pleasure of the orange, the glossy look of chestnuts and the fun of roasting them on the fire-bars, and the varied appeals of the pomegranate; and I knew that when I had decided and had made my purchase I would wish I had made some other.

At the sweets-shop the problem was more intense, the possibilities reached almost the hundred. Almond-rock had a finer flavour than coconut-toffee, but for a penny you got only two ounces of almond-rock, while of coconut-toffee you got four ounces. And there were all the other things—coconut-ice, clove-stick, locusts, bull's-eyes, bouncers, all-sorts, brandy-balls, Chinese cushions, liquorice-strips, Chicago caramels, Pontefract comfits, crystallized chips, pop-corn, barley-sugar, colt's-foot-rock, marzipan, burnt almonds. Of some of the humbler of these the smaller shops would serve farthing's-worths. In summer you could get for a halfpenny a glass of sherbet-and-water, and in winter a hot fruit-drink; and there were other tempting things than those for the stomach.

There were prize-packets. There were Transfers with their gorgeous colours, a halfpenny a sheet. At a halfpenny you could get little glass-covered boxes containing a tortoise made of gelatine; when you set the box on the palm of your hand, the head and legs would wiggle. Again at a halfpenny you could get a box of coloured matches which burnt with flames of red, green and blue, and at the same price you could get twelve " throw-downs "—little twists of coloured paper filled with a pinch of some explosive substance; you flung them to the ground, preferably behind an elderly man, and they went off with a report like that of a Chinese cracker. Also at a halfpenny you could get a butterfly, five sizes larger than life, made of some gauze material; that, too, went on the palm of your hand whose warmth set it opening and closing its wings. Still at a halfpenny you could get a toy pistol, and at another halfpenny a box of " caps "; or a large cardboard bumble-bee with elastic wound about it, and a long piece of string to it by which you whirled it about your head and caused it to produce a convincing hum.

After a final spell of anxious consideration I acquired from the High Street confectioner's a prize-packet, and from the newsagent's the *Funny Wonder*. Then I turned off to a side street sweets-shop for some crystallized coconut chips and a clove-stick. Then back to the High Street grocer's for a bag of broken wafers. Then to another side-street shop for an ounce of all-sorts and an ounce of coconut-toffee. And so my two-pence-halfpenny was spent:

1 Prize Packet	... ...	½d.
The Funny Wonder	...	½d.
1 oz. coconut chips	...	¼d.
1 clove-stick	... ...	¼d.
Bag of wafers	... ...	½d.
1 oz. all-sorts	... ...	¼d.
1 oz. coconut-toffee	...	¼d.
		2½d.

And to remember to-day what twopence-halfpenny could then purchase is to remember marvels out of what seems to be a lost fairyland.

That little carnival of Saturday Morning was followed always by the larger carnival of Saturday Night, when the family shopping was done. The High Street then was a different High Street. As a child I saw the streets at different hours as possessed not only by people and traffic and shops but by the spirit of those hours. Morning gave everything a touch of its own quality; I couldn't name it but I knew what it was and that it was distinct from the quality given by Afternoon. And Afternoon's quality or tinge was quite other than that which displaced it and took possession of the streets under the name of After Dark.

That Saturday Night the High Street, whose pulse for me beat always high with romance, was astir with an extra rush of light and life. Shops which on other nights closed at ten were open till midnight, and they were Saturday Night shops; mood and movement were heightened and accelerated. The butcher's straw hat and blue apron were those he always wore, but they assumed an air of being properties of revelry. The greengrocer's chanted invitation had not the purely commercial note of everyday; that, too, held a ring of festival. The whole street seethed with a rich and fruity flush of life charged to the overflow with the spirit of English Saturday Night.

It was a scene that came fresh to me every Saturday; the first sight of it never failed to go tingling through me with the bliss of music. I had last seen it in the afternoon, dressed in thin sun and mist. At this later hour it was something new, washed and polished, like myself, in its evening best, and making with its glitter and shine a hospitable contrast to the windy waste of the Green—a dark solitude of trees and ponds and bushes which lay between the top of the High Street and the next suburb.

All the shops, great and small, were in full doing, and the

pavements were twinkling with the in-and-out movements of shoppers and young strollers, and the roadway was sending up a rumble from carts, trams, buses and broughams, and there was the jingle of hansom-cab bells and the elfin artillery of bicycle bells. The main crowd moved about two points at the centre of either side, and the bursts of light at those points dazzled even the prodigal shops. Those points were, on one side, the Imperial Palace of Varieties, and on the other the Crystal Arcade, glass-covered, fitted with white shops, and lavishly lit by electric light, making a corridor of damask and pearl between the High Street and the parish church.

To the shop-lights of orange or lemon were added the white flares of the naphtha lamps of the stalls and all their hot noise. There were the oyster-stall (oysters sixpence a dozen); the sweets stall, where sweets were made on the restricted premises; the baked potato-stall; the sarsaparilla stall; the saveloy and pease-pudding stall; the colporteur's stall, descendant of the seventeenth-century chapman or flying stationer, with religious booklets and texts; the toy stall; the cough-lozenge stall. At every other corner was an entertainment—the Calculating Horse, a Salvation Army meeting, a nigger troupe, a German Band. On vacant spaces were a Highland sword-dancer, a thought-reader, a phrenologist. And there was my favourite—the Peep Show. This was a large glass-fronted box, and for a halfpenny the owner would remove the cover from the window, and through it you saw a model village in which, at the touch of a button, everything came alive. The trees waved, the cattle nodded their heads, cottage-doors opened and figures slid to the threshold, water ran down the mill-wheel, the windmill sails revolved, the grinding-stone revolved, and a figure at a pump worked the handle. It was a ha'porth of poetic experience. In between the stall were beggars or cripples with matches or boot-laces or silly toys, and everywhere were cheerful voices and light scuffles of feet.

And back home, at supper, when the street was still, there

K

was yet a late organ to send up to our window the grievous tunes of London comic-songs—tunes so charged with the self-mocking pathos of the London streets that they might have been the spirits of dead Londoners made into music.

*   *   *

That was one child's Saturday in a London suburb fifty years ago. The Saturday of this generation is markedly different, in features and in atmosphere. What was variegated common life has become uniform commonplace life. One suburb is much like another. Shopping is less happy-go-lucky. Amusement is restricted to a few large-scale mechanized grooves. Individual movement and expression are less fluid and free. The child of to-day can no longer get for twopence-halfpenny a comic-paper, a bag of wafers, a prize-packet, and four separate kinds of sweets; nor can he get all those free vagabond street-entertainments. And if he could he would only scorn them. He can fill his time with delights that fifty years ago would have been miracles. Yet I have no doubt that for him Saturday is still Saturday, a day apart, with a quality and colour of its own; an Uncle of a day.

James Laver

THE KINGDOM OF MICOMICON

THE hero of "Sinister Street" was fortunate at least in
this: that his nursery library included a copy of *Don
Quixote,* in the magnificent edition illustrated by Gustave Doré.
So did mine, and so was I too among the rich.

It is an enormous volume, far too heavy for the hands or
knees of a child. It needs a good stout table, preferably with
a ball-fringed table-cloth, or else a nice soft woolly hearthrug.
I did not mind which but my elders showed a marked
preference for the former and, on the whole a mild and
obedient little boy, I humoured them. For scarcely had the
book been opened and a few pages turned than I was no longer
seated at a mahogany table or stretched upon a black sheepskin
rug. I was no longer in England. In Spain, you say, but it
was a Spain that never existed, a land of castles that never were,
of cloud-capped towers and gorgeous palaces created out of
a wisp of vapour and ready to vanish in a moment.

All children know such a land whatever key may unlock
its doors; but my key was Quixote, and for that I am eternally
grateful, and, I suppose, more grateful to Doré than to
Cervantes. For, to say truth, I cherished a slight grudge against
the great Spaniard. He seemed, to my childish mind, to come
down on the wrong side of the fence; to be laughing at Quixote
when he ought to have been backing him up. I was too young
to taste the irony within the irony, too young to realize that it
was the mockers that Cervantes mocked. And so, disapproving
of the text, and skimming it, I concentrated upon the illustrations. Cervantes might disappoint me; Doré never did.

I tried to copy some of the pictures, and found it extremely difficult. There seemed to be so many lines. Even a pale grey sky was nothing but lines, close parallel lines impossible to reproduce with even the sharpest pencil. I asked one of my elders why the artist had " drawn " them like that. He answered quite correctly that what I had before me were not drawings but engravings. " Steel engravings," he added, leaving me no wiser. Indeed it was not until I became myself a keeper of Prints and Drawings that I understood the full enormity of this piece of misinformation. For, of course, the illustrations to " Quixote " are not steel engravings at all; they are wood engravings, produced when that difficult craft had reached its highest point of development.

What Doré had done was to produce a drawing in pen-line and wash. This was then handed over to Pisan, or some other whose name appeared so mysteriously in one corner of the finished product, and this superb craftsman had " translated " it into terms of wood engraving, pushing his sharp burin into the polished surface of boxwood, scooping out the lights, cutting triangular trenches in the half-shadows, laboriously crosshatching in reverse. Perhaps if I had known all this it would have increased my pleasure; perhaps it would have dissipated the magic. As I did not know it, I accepted the mystery, and gazed at the interweaving lines until my sight was dazzled and my imagination stimulated almost to the point of hypnosis.

Some of the illustrations showed market places, inns, the courtyards of castles and all the bustling life of sixteenth century Spain as Doré's imagination conceived it, hard in outline, drenched in sunlight, peopled with muleteers, soldiers and bandits. These pictures I cared for least. I preferred to follow the knightly pilgrim into the fastnesses of the Sierra Moressa, where fantastic crags encroached upon the sky, and where the clouds transformed themselves into yet more mountains. Or into the depths of forests where, with the Don, I paused to drink at the haunted stream, or rested on the greensward while

Rozinante browsed peacefully in the middle distance, and tiresome Sancho renewed once more the interminable arguments of common sense, unheard alike by Quixote and by me.

So there was built up in my mind a kind of dream-picture, a Never-Never Land which was always with me, nowhere and yet everywhere, under the closed eyelids and between the pages of a book. And as I came to other books, the elements they brought were incorporated, adding new features to my secret kingdom, extending its scope, but never modifying its essential character. Little vignettes from " Keepsakes " brought square-towered churches and crumbling ivied walls; " Illustrated Poets ", long vistas of lake and fell and forest. By and by I began to read the poems, and they had the same strange effect upon me, as by a contagious magic :

> It is the hush of night, and all between
> Thy margin and the mountains, dusk, yet clear ...

Perhaps all this was very bad for me. I was a rather lonely little boy, given more to solitary contemplation than to the companionship of my own age and kind. Cricket seemed to me the most pointless occupation ever invented and I must confess that I cling to this heretical opinion still. The object of education should be to make extraverts of us all, good-mixers, not moon-struck hermits walking in two worlds at once.

> Sith none that breatheth living air doth know
> Where is that happy land of Faery
> That I so much do vaunt, yet nowhere show ...

What a pity Doré did not illustrate Spenser! Or the Bible, or " Pilgrim's Progress ". Perhaps he did illustrate the Bible, but it never came my way. For " Pilgrim's Progress " I had to make do with a more pedestrian artist whose name I have forgotten. I am grateful to him none the less if only for that vision from the Delectable Mountains, which gave the travellers, and me, our first glimpse of the Heavenly City, with its

streets of gold, its gates of pearls, its walls of jasper. Yet lest
I should present too sugary a picture let me hasten to add that
my dream-world was not altogether untouched by darkness
and horror. Some pictures even in " Quixote " I hurried over,
turning two pages at once; and perhaps it was just as well that
I did not come upon Doré's " Dante " until a little later, when
my nerves were stronger or my sensibility less acute.

For years, the drawings of Cruickshank gave me the creeps.
His humans seemed to me to resemble insects. With quivering
antennæ, and spindly legs, a cockroach would be too creepy-
crawly to be contemplated without a shudder! And yet it was
a world which, once seen, could not be dimmed from the mind,
a world of terrifying actuality. Perhaps it was just this that
I disliked about it. Cruickshank's vision is hemmed-in,
bounded on all sides as by the lens of a microscope. What we
see is a magnified drop swarming with animalculæ. There is
no distance in Cruickshank, no vista; and I was a " vista-
monger " from my earliest years.

So was my beloved Doré. He delighted in nothing so much
as in leading the eye onwards over walls and terraces, across
rivers and mighty mountain chains. And beyond the mountains the lowering cumuli and through the gaps in the cumuli,
floating evanescent flecks, celestial shafts of gods or angels,
dazzling the eyes to look upon, and bewildering the mind with
the contemplation of infinity. One such picture in " Quixote "
is with me even now, although years have passed since I opened
the volume. It depicts the eternal pair setting forth on I know
not what new expedition and adventure, very small in a vast
and rocky landscape, while above them arches a sky full of
fantastic shapes. " Onward," says the legend—" Onward to the
Kingdom of Micomicon." I had no need to follow them; for
Doré had given me the key, and I dwelt there already.

Howard Spring

FAIRWATER DAYS

WHEN Mr. Lloyd George became an Earl, Jack the Giant-killer sitting down comfortably at the giant's table—as is the usual way of the world at last—with no more rising of the hackles at a grumbled Fe, Fi, Fo, Fum, a newspaper instructed us that it was characteristic of this great man to have associated with his title the name of a simple rivulet. Lloyd George of Dwyfor. . . .

But in truth there was nothing remarkable about this. It is the property of youth to long for the fullness of years and power; and nothing becomes age so much as its instinctive turning back to con again the white unsullied page of infancy.

Those who advance into great years have often remarked that while the things of yesterday quickly fade from memory, the things of long ago take an increasingly hard sharp outline, so that the face of a mother long dead, that bent over a cradle, is nearer and dearer than many a face not seen perhaps till after that other was dust.

This we may take to be a happy arrangement of nature, joining our end and our beginning in two serenities, wherein all that there may have been of too much heat and rancour in our middle time is diminished to its due proportion in both a forward and a backward perspective.

Thus, in those estuary years, sharp and salty with tidal premonitions of the last great wisdom, it is not unusual to hark back beyond the years of boulders and boiling cataracts to the sweet innocent waters of the source; and that man is to be counted fortunate who, in fact as well as metaphor, can listen in age to the sound of young water that was in his infant ears.

Whether my own dear childhood stream would be there to meet me, were I now to set out upon its re-discovery, I cannot say. Irk and Irwell, that once flashed and twinkled and were merry with trout, are now in manacles and lead a life that is largely subterranean and wholly subdued. It may be that a like indignity has befallen my happy brook that was full of cresses and clean pebbles; but I think it may, thus far, have escaped with lesser mishaps. That it is not the stream it was is certain, for, all about that part of my native place, there has been a great increase of houses; but, if I may judge from a swift glance I was permitted when motoring that way some years back, there remains a justification for the name of the district.

In that name there is a tribute to my stream, a salute to its power through many generations to bring joy and refreshment, for the village it laves is called Fairwater. I cannot say how far Fairwater was from the place we lived in, for the laggard and dilatory way of a child will make a mile of what is to others a crossing of the road; but, in memory, to go to Fairwater had all the enchantment of an enterprise. It was something to be decided upon beforehand, to be prepared for, and then to be carried out, as, before circumnavigating a continent, a mariner would see that his ship was provisioned and well-founded.

It is one of the happy circumstances of my memory of Fairwater that all its days are sunny. No doubt, to those who lived there, Fairwater can recall cloud as well as sunshine, days when the aspens shivered not only with their own secret ecstasy but also with the cold caress of rough winds; days, maybe, when ice muted the water and stilled the perpetual quiet chuckle that, for me, is ever in its throat. But none of that is known to me. "For ever wilt thou love, and she be fair." It was unthinkable to go to Fairwater except when the primroses bloomed in their buttery clusters upon the railway embankment beneath which the water babbled; or when the hot hushed days of June were cooled by the water's liquid music, and the dog-daisies stared exhausted and white-eyed at the sky's aching blue; or when, in autumn, there were rough russet nuts to be gathered from the hazels, or horse-chestnuts sending their varnished gleam through the split sides of their sheaths, prickly to the intruder, but full of mealy softness for the protection of the nut's exquisite satin.

On some such day we would awake, with the knowledge slowly dawning behind our sleepy eyes that this was the day on which we were to go to Fairwater! With what anxiety would the window-square, already full of light, be examined for its prognostic of the day's weather! Save the desirable affirmation that it was a fine day, not much was to be gleaned, for the window looked on no prospect more heartening than the high wall of a building wherein, these being the days before motor-cars, tradesmen's carts, and sprightly gigs, and stylish pompous carriages for the wealthy were built. Nor from any other than the bedroom window was there fairer prospect. We were on all hands house-bound.

But it was enough that the sky was blue. Fairwater itself would supply all else that was needful to a day's bliss. And so, with breakfast behind us, and with our dinner in our pockets, we would be seen forth by our mother, who no doubt welcomed Fairwater days from her own low angle of producing a little domestic peace.

Where we lived was, then, on the westward fringes of the town. Soon it would be a town no longer; it would dignify itself with the name of city, and attest its new magnificence by an ever wider and wider sprawl. Thus, I think, where then we were almost at once among fields, with the hedges powdered by the wayside dust that this generation does not know, you would not now find fields at all, and I imagine you could almost come to Fairwater itself without encountering our familiar and cherished landmarks.

It was, I suppose, fitting that in this innocent world there should, as in a good fairytale, be a hint of the ogre; and this, for us, was provided by the knowledge that that sweet name—Fairwater—had been lent to a crime that but lately had filled the columns of the local Press. "The Fairwater Murder". So the headings had run upon the page, and when all that coil and agitation had died away, there remained as it were a delicious wraith of horror shuddering among the trees, the faint but fatal hiss of a hidden serpent in our Eden. It had been a shooting affair, and there were those who said that upon one of the noble roadside elms the mark of a bullet was to be seen. We would search for it, allowing the blight of that still raw tragedy to seep darkly through the joy of our excursion. But, sweet heaven! what pocks and indentations an ancient elm may bear. The scars of all the years had carved their intricate and antique geography up and down every notched and knotted trunk, so that, if these were evidence, a thousand had fallen at our right hand and ten thousand at our left!

It was not, in any case, to be imagined that darkness could reign over light on a Fairwater day. Here were the cottages whose situation had perpetual charm. Our lovely stream tinkled along one side of the village street. Here and there it was bridged with long flat stones, and on the farther side of each of these bridges was a garden gate, and beyond that a path leading to a cottage door. Always, in my memory, the cottage gardens are gay with innocent anonymous flowers, for, beyond a common few, the names of flowers were unknown to me. Never, I thought, could cottages be lovelier than these or situated more romantically, each with its own little bridge leaping across the singing water.

And here let me pause to point out that my stream has not even a name. It is not so much as a Dwyfor. It is but a trickle of water through a village street, over a pebbly bed that kept it fresh and gay, down a lane that was then but a foot-track, where it hugged a hedge-bottom and then flowed into the Ely river, itself no more than an insignificant thread upon even a big map. But what power it had to cheer and to charm, its voice no more in the vast orchestration of waters than a wren's twitter in the hedgerow chorus of May! It was nicely apportioned to our infant demands. There was no place where a child's foot could not safely cross it. Its greatest traffic was of minnows; a trout therein would have been Leviathan; its most splendid visitants were the dragonflies that rustled their stiff metallic wings over its pigmy eddies among the musk and watercress.

Such was my stream that to me was the essence and epitome of all joys, out under the sun of summer. From the spot where its slabbed bridges crossed to the cottage gates it flowed away down the side lane, and it was here that it became wholly ours. For in the lane there was but one house, and no one seemed ever to be stirring in it or about it. You could spend a day in the lane with no fear that a footstep would disturb the drowsy spell or any voice but your own break upon the enchanted air.

This, then, was our place, my brother's and mine, the place to which my thought turns often back, mine only now that he is, long since, gone; my Dwyfor, my Abana or my Pharpar, better than all the waters of Israel.

There we would eat the wrapped provisions we had brought and drink our bottle of water, and with our shoes off cool our feet in the sweetly-moving stream. We would fish for the tiny catches such water could provide, and, with the help of a natural history book, peep and botanise for hours on end. Or, for hours on end, we would lie upon the bank, listening to the hot drone of summer threaded by the stream's cool singing.

Such was the beginning, and who would complain if life's full circle should fetch up at last upon so innocent an end?

COKE OVENS

Norman Janes

Walter Greenwood

MUTINEER

ONE boy of my childhood acquaintance, whom I shall call Nobby, was accursed. He was the eldest of what proved to be an enormous family. Every year his mother presented to his dispirited father the "latest" whose yowlings in the "cribbed, cabined, confined" area of the Salford cottage in which they lived made the day (and night) hideous and intolerable to the harassed mother.

One of the expedients adopted by mothers of that time (and, maybe, this for all I know) was to dip a rubber dummy into a pennyworth of a syrupy drug and plop it into the contorted, toothless O with the exasperated remark : "*There* y'are."

One defect of this device was that it cost money and, as any old Salford or Manchester lady will tell you, pennies sometimes were very difficult to come by in the year 1910.

Nobby, my accursed friend, was well aware of this (as we all were from bitter experience). As a consequence he made himself scarce the moment his watchful eye or attentive ear caught the first movement or preliminary screech of "the latest". Many a time when we, "the lads," were gadding off on some adventure he would be saddled with a squalling child in a ricketty pram with the instruction to "mind him". Instantly the 'gang' would turn on him like wolves on a wounded companion to warn him, quite unnecessarily, that "You can't run wi' that." We knew quite well, as all Small Boys intuitively know, that the world was in conspiracy against us. Whatever we did was sure to be wrong and all our excursions ended by having to "run for it."

Many a time when setting off with the lads I glanced back to see Nobby standing by the bawling child in the pram bawling himself, threatening the little innocent: " Shurrup or I'll murder you. It's all through you."

Out of necessity Nobby developed the supernatural power of disappearance. The lads would be absorbed in a game on the pavement, Nobby amongst us, when, on a sudden, Nobby's mother would be standing in front of us demanding his presence. We would look around us to find that Nobby, like the ghost of Hamlet's father, had gone. It was only then that we heard the screaming of an infant. Mama, infuriated, would announce to us all: " I'll murder him when I see him."

I do not think I ever saw poor Nobby in the presence of his Mother but what she either was wagging an admonishing finger at him or fulfilling her inevitable promise to " fetch him a back hander." The whole street knew when the latter had been presented for he always appeared, hand to ear, bawling his grief at the top of his voice.

I was the recipient of his confidences which were given in the seclusion of a storage yard nearby. This agreeable place was protected from trespassers by a high wall in the bricks and mortar of which we had knocked and chipped finger and toe holds.

By degrees maternal tyranny got the better of Nobby and, one day, his mother came to ask had I seen him. As I had not I said so. His mother reported to mine that he had been absent hours, concluding with the usual threat of murder when he reappeared. I sneaked out and went to where I knew he would be.

I found Nobby crouched in the corner of a big packing case. In answer to my question as to what had happened he told me that he was a mutineer and concluded: " An' I'm not goin' back."

" Eh? " I replied.

" I've run away from 'ome," he said.

I regarded him with a holy respect, crawled into the packing case and sat down at his side. " Are you goin' to live in here? " I asked him, enviously. His answer was staggering : " No," he said; then, after a moment's pause : " I'm goin' to Blackpool."

It should be remarked that, to us, Blackpool was a fabulous place. We sometimes saw grown-ups in the finery of their Sunday best, carrying suitcases. Mostly they were newly married couples and all the street turned out to cheer their self-conscious departure to Blackpool. One of the favourite excursions of the gang was to go to Dawney's Hill which overlooks the Irwell Valley on the Bolton Road to watch the trains scream-ing along. To us all of them were " expresses " and all of them were going " to Blackpool."

In the whole of the seven and a half years of Nobby's existence I do not think he had created such an impression on anybody as he did on me by his declaration. I did not know that a bigger shock was impending for, when I made the very natural inquiry as to how he proposed to get there, he answered : " Walk it."

" But," I stuttered : " You don't know the road."

" Yis, I do," he answered.

" Where? " I demanded, knowing he could not possibly answer.

I was wrong. " Along t' train lines," he said, adding " Bringle 'eath," by which he referred to the Brindle Heath railway sidings at the foot of Dawney's Hill and over which we used to fly our kites in the prevailing westerly winds.

I could not think of anything to say. I could only stare with a respect utter and profound.

Suddenly he crawled out of the packing case and looked down at me : " Well," he said, coolly : " I'm off. " There was a short pause : he added : " Comin'? "

" Me? " I countered.

" Aye," he answered.

"I—I——," I stammered. After all, there was no reason why I had to go, was there?

"Yah!" he jeered. "You're afraid, that's what *you* are. Afraid."

I was out of the packing case in a second glaring at him and demanding "Who is?"

"You are."

"Come on," I replied.

"All right, then," he said: "Come on."

So we had to go.

We climbed over the wall and set off towards Brindle Heath railway sidings neither speaking since I, for one, was far too busy trying to find an excuse wherewith to extricate myself, without loss of face, from the adventure upon which I had been foolish enough to embark.

Nobby kept sneaking glances at me and I at him.

Up Church Street, across Broad Street, down Brindle Heath Road and over the sleeper fence. And now we were on railway property. There, in front of us, were hundreds upon hundreds of stationary railway trucks on the network of rusty sidings. Beyond, on the high embankment, a passenger train shrilled derisively on its whistle as it clattered by.

Ordinarily when the gang ventured to trespass here the pleasure always was spoiled by the appearance of a "feller" with a stick, in the person of a railway employee. On this occasion nobody could have been more welcome than the "feller" to put an end to the ridiculous situation. But, naturally, when his presence was most needed he was not to be seen.

Hopefully, Nobby asked: "Is he there?"

Aha, I thought, Nobby's capitulating. So I replied, firmly: "No," and added: "Come on," hoping by this to undermine Nobby's resolve. To my disappointment he followed my lead; so I had to whip up my own courage by telling myself that while he kept to it so would I. We dodged into the midst of the vast assembly of railway trucks. I was horrified at the thought of the monsters being coupled to an engine and set into motion. Everything about them had an air of having been made for the sole purpose of the destruction of small boys. We walked on down the seemingly interminable aisle and then, simultaneously, we saw it.

A kite.

A beauty. Shop bought, not home made. Coloured tissue paper on a fine cane frame, tailings yards long. There it was, this beautiful creation, caught by the tail to the top of a railway truck. There it was, hanging down like a wounded thing, the sport of every errant breeze.

Neither of us spoke. We both slyly increased our speed each hoping the other would not notice the acceleration. Faster, faster and faster as though we had entered the Manchester to Blackpool walking race. Finally there was no sense any longer in keeping up the pretence and, at this point, it became a downright sprint. The prize was too great for either of us to be the loser. We arrived neck and neck, hands outstretched. Both together, having clutched it, we exclaimed: "I saw it first!"

The tailings parted. Neither of us would loose hold though each denounced the other's roughness.

"Leave go, you'll smash it."

"*You* leave go. It's mine."

It was a big kite and its tissue paper acted as a screen between our faces. We quarrelled with each other through this paper flimsiness; then, as though to settle the matter and to my utmost astonishment, Nobby's fist crashed through the paper and hit me square upon the nose.

"Oooo!" I exclaimed, indignantly: "You—you——!" Then my fist went through and hit *him* on the nose. "Ow!" he yelled, and kicked me on the shin, so I kicked him back. By this time the thing of beauty was no longer a joy but a ruin. I glared at him and exclaimed: "You're a rotten thief." We now held a stick each of the delicate frame.

L

He was about to make a suitable answer to my accusation when I saw the initial word freeze on his lips as his eyes were attracted by something behind me. He turned tail and ran. I turned to look. It was the " feller ", stick in hand, coming hot foot for us.

" Copped you *this* time," he shouted, prematurely. I flew. It was a race; like Tam o' Shanter's with the witches after him; only that, in my case, the keystone of the bridge was the sleeper fence. Once over that and I was safe.

The " feller " was within arm's reach of me. I was all out. I saw Nobby six yards away scrambling over the fence to safety. I made a supreme effort, took a flying leap and, as my backside was about to disappear over the top the " feller's " stick came across it with a hearty whack.

When I landed on my feet the infuriating Nobby was yards away *laughing*! To make matters worse he called out " Yaaah! " at *me*! Maddened, I dashed at him and chased him all the way home but did not catch him. I saw him dash into his home and heard his clumping boots echoing down the bare lobby. My resentment was so fierce that I shouted my intention to wait for him to " come out."

I had forgotten that he was a mutineer : I had forgotten that he had " run away " from home : I had forgotten his mother's promise to " half-murder " him on his return. When I was chasing him I did not satisfy myself with the knowledge that he was running from me into a greater danger. I was only reminded of this when to my immense and unchristian-like satisfaction I heard a loud slap and an even louder howl of anguish from within. Nobby made an immediate reappearance, a milk jug in one hand, the other hand clapped to his ear, his mouth wide open and contorted in agony, tears running down his face.

" Serves you right," I shouted : " And I'll ne'er go to Blackpool wi' *you* no more."

A CORNER OF THE FOREST

Ethelbert White

A. P. Herbert

NANNY

I SING a long-neglected dame.
Let plays and poets all proclaim
The wonder of the Mother's name
    And even that of Granny;
Let others tell with loud hurrahs
The general praises of Papas—
I hymn the Mother of Mammas,
    I sing the British Nanny.
Not every pink and girlish thing
    That pushes round a pram,
The ancient rock-like NURSE I sing,
    Britannia's virgin dam,
That, old as mountains and as stout,
From child to child is passed about
Till, childless yet, she passes out,
    The lonely British Nanny.

For she it was that from the first
Refused to judge us by our worst;
We might be yelling fit to burst,
    She crooned a cheerful ditty;
Our very Aunts could not deny
That we were small and ugly fry,
But she with fond prophetic eye
    Maintained that we were pretty.
Alone of all the human race
    She took the kind of view

Of our importance, brain and face,
    That we would have men do;
And I can never quite forget
No other person I have met
Considered me a perfect pet,
    So here's a health to Nanny!

The artless prattle of a child
Drives nearly everybody wild;
And who that for an hour beguiled
    A babe, however clever,
For all the riches of the rich
Would undertake a life in which
They lived at that exacting pitch
    Ten hours a day for ever?
Though even in the mother's joys
    A grander cycle dawns
When we grow more like little boys
    And less like little prawns,
Our Nanny, in a nobler strain
Would have us at our worst remain,
A babe for ever pink and plain,
    Herself for ever Nanny.

Alas! the twig becomes a bough;
We do not need a Nanny now;
Forgotten her who showed us how,
    We walk to death or glory;
And whether Fate blows cold or hot,
Whatever women shape our lot,
It's safe to say a Nurse will not
    Be mentioned in the story.
Some other baby far away
    Is hers to soothe or slap,
Some NELSON'S in the bath to-day,
    Some SHELLEY in her lap;

And when I think on this small star
How many mighty men there are,
I call for wine and drain a jar
    To England's noble Nannies.

Gerald Bullett

THE LAMB YARD

THE older sisters, Alice and Kate, stood little John on the table in his new sailor-suit, and, hovering near lest he should threaten to fall, admired him vociferously. Rose, five years old, was as excited as either of them. But her rapture spent itself in gazing: she had nothing to say. Under cover of the general enthusiasm Johnny lifted up a thoughtful foot and with delicate deliberation planted it on the edge of the *crepe de Chine* of which Alice was making herself a new blouse. The boy stood on the grape machine, he said to himself. His exploit went unnoticed.

"My word, Johnny, you *are* a smart boy!" cried Alice. "And to-morrow I'll bring you home a lanyard!" This yard was as long as her arm; Alice was a telephonist and had been trained to speak with laborious distinctness.

These elder sisters were old indeed. They went every day to the City just as Father did; and in their lunch hours they consumed buns and milk, as Father did not. Alice was the more seasoned wage-earner; but Kate, too, had put her hair up and contrived to look older than her seventeen years. They all lived with their parents at 117 Crystal Palace Avenue, the house that had a street lamp just in front of it. On winter evenings Rose and Johnny seldom missed seeing the lamp-lighter come, with his magic pole; and it was Johnny's pleasure, which he was shy of sharing even with Rose, to steal into his parents' bedroom, after dusk, to see the light from this lamp filtering through the slats of the brown venetian blinds and the network of the lace curtains, sending queer patterns slanting across the lino. It was a house of seven rooms, with a square patch of garden in front and an oblong patch behind. Two steps led to the front door, and these Mother cleaned herself, in secret, after dark, not liking the neighbours to see her at it; for some of the neighbours were better off and employed wan little creatures called stepper-girls to perform that menial task. In the front garden there was a rhododendron bush and a mountain ash. In the back garden Father grew roses and cucumbers, lupins and marigolds, vegetable marrows in a glass frame, and a bed of cress which sometimes mysteriously assumed the shape of people's initials, the people in question being John and Rose. It was Johnny who had mixed up the cucumbers with the flowers; for one day he had found some flat white seeds in a brown paper bag in the tool-shed, and thoughtfully planted one of them, to see what would happen. And what happened was a cucumber, nestling among the primulas and shaded by tea-roses.

There was not an inch of wasted space in the garden. Nor in the house either. The drawing-room, which had French windows commanding a nice view of the drains, was full of a yellow-keyed piano which Father had picked up cheap at a sale. In the dining-room hung a brightly coloured picture of the new king, Edward the Seventh. In the kitchen, John's favourite resort, there was a toy cupboard, there was a rocking-horse, there was an inaccessible mantelshelf accommodating a row of wooden bins for flour, oatmeal, brown sugar, and other comestibles. The kitchen also contained a stove, upon which, under supervision, one might roast chestnuts on days of special festivity; a deal table with a drawer full of interesting things such as corks, labels, and a vast tangle of string; a dresser hung with teacups; and six chairs, any two of which would serve as coach-and-horses, a sledge, or what you will, for people who wished to drive through Siberian forests pursued by wolves.

And to these everyday joys was to be added another, inconceivably beautiful.

Alice and Kate, competing for the honour, lifted John down from the table and began divesting him of his sailor-suit; for it was his bedtime. Rose, by virtue of her seniority, might have petitioned to stay up another half-hour; but she was an obliging child, and knowing by experience that John wished for her company she waived her rights and made ready to accompany him. " I'll bring you home a lanyard," Alice had said. And what Alice promised, that she would perform, having a better memory than either Kate or Mother. Johnny, not liking to be divorced from his new suit, had already forgotten Alice's promise. But Rose had not forgotten it. She was rapt in the prospect of a happiness too wonderful for belief. Alice is bringing Johnny a lamb-yard. So ran her enchanted thought. Would they, she wondered, be real lambs, or wooden ones? She would contrive to make shift with either, and to hope for real ones was taking a big risk. For a moment she wavered. But desire, outrunning discretion, soon changed into belief, transporting her to a day-dream in which young woolly lambs with soft black noses skipped and baa-ed about her in their pleasant fold. She and John, living in the same world, a world which the others could not enter, held many of their possessions in common. It was therefore safe to assume that she would be allowed to love the lambs in the lamb-yard as furiously as he himself would certainly do. As furiously, and with greater constancy, for John, less mature than she, was at present more fickle in his passions.

When they were both tucked up in bed, and the candle had been blown out, and the putters-to-bed had gone downstairs to enjoy the mysterious activities that grown-ups engage in after six in the evening, Rose put the point to him in unequivocal terms.

" I say, Johnny!"

Johnny, having concerns of his own, paid no heed to her soft drowsy voice. While she waited in vain for his answer, scraps of his murmuring meditations became faintly audible to her :

The boy stood on,
The boy stood on,
The boy stood on,
The grape machine.
Half a yard of grape machine.
The boy stood on the grape machine.

Rose tried again. "Oh *Johnny!*" She gently shook him. She was urgent. Sleepiness had left her. "Will you let me play with the lambs in your lamb-yard? Will you, Johnny?"

She heard her voice as though it were some other person's voice. The bed was warm; Johnny's body was warm beside her; the friendly darkness enclosed them both. Her voice, though she spoke softly, seemed loud and clear.

"Yes," answered Johnny absently. After a pause he suddenly said: "What say?"

She repeated her prayer. Johnny said: "What's a lamb-yard?"

"A lamb-yard," said Rose, "is a yard with lambs in it."

"White lambs?" asked Johnny. "Like in a field?"

"Yes, white lambs," said Rose confidently. "With black noses," she added on an afterthought. "Won't it be lovely?"

". . . half a yard of grape machine . . ."

"Johnny, you're not listening. Won't it be lovely, I say?"

"What say?" said John.

"The lamb-yard. The lovely lamb-yard."

"What lamb-yard?"

"The one Alice is going to bring you to-morrow."

"Oh! . . . Will there be lambs in it?"

Rose, a patient sister, went over the ground again. By persevering, she infected John with the excitement that possessed her own heart and mind. They exchanged dazzling conjectures. How many lambs would there be? Would they keep them in the kitchen or the garden? Would they eat Father's flowers? What would Mother say? Perhaps there would be seven lambs. Perhaps there would be nine.

" How many do you think? "

" I should think about ten," said Rose judicially.

" How many is ten? "

" Twice five," said Rose proudly.

It was a conclusive answer. Johnny, though he didn't understand it, seemed profoundly satisfied. When Rose spoke again he was asleep.

Soon Rose herself was asleep. And then, almost at once it seemed, she was awake again, opening her eyes in the light of the new morning. It was Saturday, which meant that the big sisters would be early home from their lordly occupations in the City. She sat at the breakfast table watchfully, with shining eyes. She could not keep her happiness secret, but she kept its cause secret, being too shy to speak of what the day meant to her. When her mind put the question she did not quite dare to believe that the lambs would be real lambs; but most of the time she forgot caution and gave herself unreservedly to her daydream, going after breakfast into the back garden, which, in her fancy, was already crowded with young skipping lambs. They nibbled the parsley. They rolled among the nasturtiums. They leapt over the lupins. Rose ran into the house crying, " Johnny! Johnny! Come and help with the lambs! They're getting through the fence into Mrs. Jones's!" And when Mother wanted to know what all the commotion was about, and what lambs, and where, and how, she kept her secret still, answering with hypocritical meekness that it was only a game.

Only a game it was, as yet. But when Alice came home, ah then. . . . ! Even to Johnny she said nothing more of the promised beatitude, seeing him already blissfully content with the new game. Playing with imaginary lambs gave Johnny abundant excuse for running, shouting, and pretending, the activities he most enjoyed.

So much for the lambs. Rose was more than satisfied with them. But what of the yard? Alice had said a lamb-*yard*; and Rose was a little vague about the yard. Perhaps it was only a way of speaking. Perhaps the garden itself was the yard. Or the kitchen. Or Johnny's play-pen. Anyhow it didn't matter, so long as there was no mistake about the lambs.

Saturday, for these children, was a day of mixed blessings. It was pleasant to have Alice and Kate home early, to say nothing of Father, who would let you mess about in the garden with him on fine days, pulling up weeds, collecting slugs, and snipping off dead blooms here and there. But on Saturday, for the late midday meal, the tired remains of the weekly joint were converted into ferocious and unappetizing objects called rissoles, and there was boiled rice instead of a real pudding. Johnny did not remember such things. He looked neither before nor after, and the boiled rice came always as a lamentable surprise to him. With Rose it was different. She was beginning to learn the grown-up vice of anticipating trouble. But to-day she had no forebodings. She knew that at half-past-two the whole family would meet round the kitchen-table for dinner; but rissoles and boiled rice could find no room in an imagination filled with the glory that was Alice.

Father arrived home first, and then Kate.

" Come, children," said Mother. " We'll make a start. Have you washed your hands, Rosie? Have you washed Johnny's hands? "

" Where's Alice? " asked Kate.

" She's late to-day," said Mother. " Never mind. I'll keep something hot for her. Now, shut your eyes, Rosie. Put your hands together, Johnny dear. And Father'll say grace."

Rose began to be afraid. The crumbs of rissole she forced down her throat proved harder than ever to swallow. What could have happened to delay Alice? Was she having trouble with the lambs? It had not occurred to her until this moment that ten lambs might be difficult to manage in a railway carriage. Her experience of such journeys was small.

But at last came the expected sound, the sound of Alice's latch-key in the front door. And a moment later—yet what a long moment it seemed!—Alice herself burst into the kitchen, hot, cross, complaining of her own lateness. There was no sign of the lamb-yard. Rose could only suppose she had left it in the hall. But why couldn't one hear the lambs bleating? was it possible that they were only wooden ones after all?

When Alice's ill humour had subsided, and still nothing to the point had been said, Rose could endure the suspense no longer. Blushing, near to tears, she plucked at her sister's sleeve and whispered.

" What is it, ducky? " said Alice, bending down to her.

" The lamb-yard for Johnny. You haven't . . . you haven't forgotten it, have you, Alice? "

" No fear!" said Alice. " 'Scuse me, Mum!" She jumped up from the table, bounced into the hall, and in a moment was back again, with a loop of white plaited cord in her hand. " There, Johnny!" she said, holding it up for his admiration. " What a smart boy you'll be now!"

Glad of any distraction from food, Johnny received the lanyard gleefully and began playing with it.

" What is it? " asked Rose, in a very small voice. " Alice, what is that thing? "

" It's a lanyard," Alice explained. " It's what sailors have round their necks to hang their knives on."

" I want a knife," announced Johnny, with firm decision.

Johnny seemed to have forgotten about the lambs. Perhaps he had never understood.

Rose said, " Where are the lambs, Alice? "

The question went unnoticed. Mother was briskly serving the children with their portions of boiled rice. Father remained grimly silent, shovelling food into his mouth.

" I want a knife," said Johnny, raising his voice. " Want a knife, want a knife, want a knife." He began hammering with his spoon on the table.

For a while no one noticed that Rosie was sitting with averted face, quietly crying.

"What's the matter, child?" asked Mother.

The child could not answer. Tears fell on her plate. She tried to cover her face with her hair. The need of a handkerchief became urgent.

"Come now!" said Mother. "Eat your nice pudding, darling. Be *quiet*, Johnny! You can't *have* a knife."

Rosie through her sobs, was heard to say something about lambs.

"There aren't any lambs, Rosie," said Alice, in a voice of comfort. "Don't be frightened. There aren't any lambs."

The sobbing subsided. "I see," said Rosie. She saw. She saw everything. She saw the hollowness of human existence.

"Now eat your nice pudding," coaxed Mother, "there's a good girl."

For answer Rosie lifted her plate high in air and with great deliberation poured its contents over the table. No lambs; no rice pudding. She sat rigid, waiting for the storm to break.

Ethel Mannin

THE TOY ENGINE

IN the almoner's office there were always toys to give away after Christmas. People brought them to the hospital round about Christmas time, though there was no children's ward, and the Lady Almoner always received them gratefully because so often when mothers came to see her they had children with them, and apart from all else a toy would keep a child quiet whilst she and the mother had a little necessary chat.

So when Peter's mother, who had been in several times about her teeth, came back in January to pay the balance of the money, as arranged, the Lady Almoner smiled at Peter and then murmured, " The engine," to her clerk. The almoner's clerk nodded and went to the cupboard where the toys were kept. She entirely approved her chief's decision. Peter was about five, and a nice bright-looking little boy, and it would have been a pity to give the toy, so beautifully made by an N.F.S. man in his spare time, to a child who wouldn't appreciate it. She took the wooden railway engine from the cupboard and stood it on the Lady Almoner's desk. It was streamlined, and painted red and green, and you could tell just by looking at it that it was an ' express '. . . .

The Lady Almoner smiled again at Peter.

" Isn't that a lovely railway engine? Would you like to have it? "

The face of Peter's mother flushed with pleasure. She was a shabby, neat little woman with anxious eyes.

" Oh, thank you ever so much," she murmured, to the Lady Almoner. " It's just what he's been wanting! " She bent down to the boy, peering eagerly into his face. "Isn't that a lovely puffer-train?" she demanded. "Aren't you a lucky little boy? Say thank you to the Lady Almoner!"

But Peter, who had gone very red, merely stared fixedly. His mother gave him a little shake. It was terrible how children always showed you up in front of people!

"Say thank you!" she repeated, firmly.

It was a pity the mother was so insistent on the thank you, the Lady Almoner thought, but to say now that it didn't matter would merely confuse the child, so she coaxed:

"You'd like to have the lovely engine, wouldn't you, Peter?"

Peter remained silent, still staring.

His mother gave him a little irritated push.

"Yes please," she commanded him.

Suddenly, as though he had been pushed into speech, Peter exclaimed violently, "No!" and then, to everyone's amazement, burst into tears, burying his face in his mother's skirt.

"For goodness sake!" his mother exclaimed. As she told a neighbour afterwards, she was 'that ashamed!' She looked despairingly at the Lady Almoner. "I don't know what's up with him, I'm sure!" and then, giving Peter another shake, "Stop it! D'you hear?"

Peter merely howled more loudly. The almoner's clerk, who was fond of children, knelt down beside him and tried to pacify him. Peter's mother was increasingly confused. She'd give it him when she got home, causing an upset like this in the Lady Almoner's office!

"I'm afraid it's no use, Miss," she told the girl, apologetically. "I'll take him home. I'm ever so sorry, causing such a commotion——" She looked wildly from the girl to the Lady Almoner.

The Lady Almoner smiled her pleasant smile. "That's all right. Take him out and show him the goldfish in the tank in the entrance hall. I expect he's only shy!"

Peter's mother, glad of the excuse, hustled her humiliating son out of the office.

A few minutes later she was back, without Peter.

She said, nervously, "Peter would really like the engine! It's just that he got the idea into his head you were going to keep him here! Goodness knows why!"

"Extraordinary idea! Poor little boy!" The Lady Almoner made a sign to her assistant, who fetched the engine once more.

"Children get such ideas into their heads!" Peter's mother murmured, as she took the toy into her arms. "There's no accounting ..."

The Lady Almoner made no comment. Useless to try to explain to Peter's mother that there was nothing in a child which could not be accounted for. 'He thought you were going to keep him here!' Somewhere in that lay the clue—if one had time to go into the child's history. . . .

*   *   *

Peter's mother had for a long time resisted the idea of evacuating Peter to the country, despite the number of bombs that fell in this district. She didn't want to leave Peter's father. As she told a neighbour, "I should only be worrying myself sick all the time about Bert. You can't just go off and leave anyone you're fond of. I know some women do, but I'm not like that. So long as Bert's at the factory me and Peter are staying!"

Women who had evacuated their own children said, a little angrily, "It's not fair to the child! Doctors say its bad for the children's nervous systems, being wakened up night after night and frightened out of their wits!" Privately they wondered Peter's father didn't insist on her getting the kid away, even if she didn't go herself.

Finally Peter's father did insist. It would be miserable without them both, he admitted, but from the beginning of the

M

'blitz' he had wanted Peter and Peter's mother in a place of safety—or comparative safety. When at last a bomb fell at the end of the street that, as he said, 'settled it'.

"I'd only worry meself ill over you, if I went," Peter's mother pleaded.

"Then let Peter go," said Peter's father. "Look how jumpy the kid is already! It's not fair on him. I know a place he could go to—a good place, where my pal Joe's kid is, on a farm——"

Peter's mother gave in. Bert 'meant it'; she knew that. There was that look on his face which said clearly, "If you won't take the kid—I will!"

She wrote to the woman who was looking after Joe's kid, and the woman wrote back, by return, what it had to be acknowledged was 'a very nice letter'. She would be very pleased to have Peter, she wrote; Joe's little girl who was about the same age had settled down nicely, and the two children would be company for each other. She then went on to tell Peter's mother about trains, and how her husband would meet them at the station with the trap. Peter's mother wrote another letter saying what time she would arrive, and it was all settled. All bar Peter, she thought, anxiously.

Peter was four, and he had never been parted from his mother. When his father worked on the night-shift at the factory, which he did most of the time, he even slept in his mother's bed. He didn't, really, know very much about his father. He was, as Peter's mother often admitted, half ruefully, half proudly, "A regular mother's boy!" At the back of her mind, unacknowledged, behind all the self-delusory façade of being unable to leave her husband, had been this dread of parting with the boy. Peter was such a mother's boy; he would fret. She could go with him—but then Bert would fret. She couldn't leave her husband and she couldn't part with the boy. All the same, the time had come when she had got to part with him, when she had got to break it to him that he must live

in some other place, away from her. How to tell him. . . . She
went over and over it in her mind, rehearsing possible openings.
It would be only for a few days, she would tell him, then she
would come and fetch him home. She wouldn't be able to stay
all the time because of poor Daddy up here all alone. . . . Let
him think she would stay a little while. Tell him she was just
going to pop back home to see how Daddy was and then she
would come for him next day. In the country there would be
no nasty old guns waking him up at night. . . . Oh, it was
no good, no good. He would howl his head off, whatever she
said. He was such a mother's boy. She couldn't tell him; she
just couldn't.

Bert was always asking her, " Broken it to the kid yet? "

At first she would admit, Not yet, she didn't like to. Oh, he
may howl at first, Bert would say, carelessly, but he'll soon get
over it. A man couldn't understand a mother's feelings, nor
a child's feelings for its mother. . . . Finally, when Bert asked
her, she evaded; it would be all right, she said, leave it to her.
Of course it'll be all right, Bert declared, and no more was said
about it.

No more was said about it and the day came when Peter's
new tooth-brush was packed in his new sponge-bag, and nothing had been forgotten—his gas-mask taken down from the
top of the wardrobe and dusted—and that hitherto remote
place, ' the country ' seemed somehow just at the end of the
road.

Peter was excited at going in the ' puffer-train ', and Bert
said, " There you are, you see—what did I say? The little
chap's actually looking forward to going! " She hadn't the
courage, then, to admit that she hadn't told the child she was
taking him to a place and coming back without him the same
day. She had written to the woman on the farm explaining
that Peter ' would only make a fuss ' if she told him beforehand she was leaving him down there, so she thought it best
she should just ' slip away ' after a while. The woman had

written back telling Peter's mother to leave it to her; she knew
how to handle children; she ought to—she had brought up
six. . . .

So the plot was all set, and Peter enjoyed the journey down,
and the ride from the station to the farm in the pony-trap, and
being lifted up, when they arrived, to see over the top of the
pig-sty's fence, and being allowed to tumble in the hay in the
barn, and watch the cows being milked. He enjoyed it all
immensely; he was happy and excited, and the lady at the
farm had all manner of wonders to show him—a fox in a
glass case, a big shell in which you could hear the sea if you
put it to your ear, a glass ball in which there was a little house,
and, if you shook it, a snow-storm. She took him by the hand
to a little room in which there were apples laid out on newspapers on the stone floor, and barrels, and big bulging sacks,
and dust and cobwebs so thick on a tiny window that you
couldn't see out, and there was a rocking-horse, and he was
lifted up into the saddle and galloped wildly—his mother
standing smiling in the doorway.

"You shall have a gallop every day," said the lady. Then,
as she lifted him down, "Now I've got something *else* to show
you," and as she said this she winked at Peter's mother, and
murmured out of the side of her mouth, "You go on ahead,
then disappear. You can get the five o'clock easy. Leave him
to me. He'll be all right now. I'll write you to-morrow.
Children soon settle down."

She turned to Peter again, smiling, holding his hand. "Now
we're going into *another* little room. . . ."

Peter's mother went on ahead down the narrow stone passage
and out at the end into the sunlight. She had a terrible guilty
sense of escape. Behind her she heard Peter repeating,
excitedly, trustingly, "*Another* little room! Something *else*
to show me. . . ." But she had no desire to turn back on the
Judas act, but only to get away—quickly—quickly—

Peter found himself in another little room.

" Just you see what we've got *here*! Isn't that a lovely puff-puff? "

It was a large wooden engine, big enough for a small child to sit in. Its red paint was shabby, and it was chipped and scarred from rough usage over a number of years. Peter stared at it, fascinated. Whilst he stared a little girl came to the door— a self-possessed little girl with short tight plaits and friendly brown eyes.

" Is that Peter? " she demanded, in a clear shrill voice.

" That's Peter," the lady said, and to Peter, encouragingly, " This is Betty, Peter. Your Daddy and her Daddy work together. Isn't that nice, now? "

" My Daddy knows your Daddy! " echoed the little girl.

" That's right," the lady said.

Peter stopped staring at the battered old wooden engine and stared at the little girl—a long, hostile stare.

" To-morrow we'll play games," the little girl announced. " Won't we? " she appealed to the lady.

" That's right," said the lady.

Peter's gaze sought beyond the little girl's round head into the darkness of the passage.

" Where's my Mummy? " There was panic in his voice.

The lady said, very gently, " Your Mummy's gone home to look after your Daddy. You wouldn't like your Daddy to be left all alone, would you now? "

Peter ran wildly to the door.

" Mummy! " he screamed. " Mummy! I want my Mummy! "

" Your Mummy's gone home, silly," said the little girl.

" That's right," the lady said, " your Mummy's gone home, and you must be a good little boy, and then to-morrow you shall ride in the nice puff-puff. . . ."

" Mummy! " Peter screamed, " Mummy! I want my Mummy! "

As the lady told her husband when he came in at supper

time, it was 'a rare business' getting the child to sleep—in fact he never would have gone off but that he sobbed himself into exhaustion. . . .

*   *   *

Peter trudged along beside his mother when they left the hospital, clutching the stream-lined engine the N.F.S. man had made so beautifully in his spare time. His face was tear-stained but triumphant.

When they were near home they met a neighbour. She stopped to speak to them and admire the engine.

"It's a beauty, and no mistake!" she declared.

Then Peter's mother explained where and how they had come by it, and the 'scene' Peter had 'created' at the hospital, first saying he didn't want it, if you please, when he wanted it all along, making her feel so ashamed. At times children were enough to drive you silly!

"He'd got some idea into his head they were going to keep him there—if you ever heard such at thing! There's simply no accounting for the ideas children get into their heads!"

"That's a fact," the neighbour murmured, sympathetically.

THE FARM ROAD

Barbara Greg

J. B. Priestley

THE SWAN SINGS TIRRALAYO

WHEN I was not in London or travelling about the country I lived in one of the six hostels that my wife runs in Herefordshire. I occupied a small bedroom and a corner attic that I had turned into a study, and I paid the hostel for my board and lodging. There were about twenty women and forty babies or small children in this particular hostel, all from the badly bombed areas. The house itself is a country mansion, with splendid gardens that supplied us with all our vegetables. It has a large and high hall, with a great open fireplace, family portraits, and the heads of animals shot in Africa on the walls. This hall is like a stage set for an old Haymarket comedy of country-house life, only it is larger. It cannot understand what is happening to it. Sometimes I sneaked in and caught it looking astounded, all the portraits and animals staring away. Several of the local gentry are like that too. You notice the same look in their eyes.

Sometimes we all moved into the hall after supper, perhaps for dancing and games or just for chatter. Sometimes we didn't bother, but hung on in the dining-room or went up to our rooms. But if there was a film show (our own silent Kodascope) or a concert, the hall was essential. It is good for music, because of all the wood panelling, and fortunately we had put our own grand piano in it. Now and then we got up a little concert ourselves, especially if my daughters were in the neighbourhood and the local doctor's sister was staying with him, for that gave us two violins and a flute, and the doctor and I could struggle along with the piano parts. But once or twice we had proper concerts. We had one provided for us by three excellent musicians, who were travelling round the countryside giving concerts for CEMA.

We had the concert proper before supper. (The three musicians were staying the night with us.) Lots of women from the village turned up in reply to our invitation. All our mothers and staff were there. There was a pianist, a violinist, and a soprano, and between them they gave us some Purcell, Bach, Mozart, Arne, Debussy, de Falla, and some folk tunes. There were also some beautiful settings for voice and unaccompanied violin by Holst, of medieval poems that I had never heard before, and to which, to my surprise, some of our evacuated mothers took a fancy. I was surprised because I imagined that to their ears this would seem very remote and astringent stuff. Among the poems was the exquisite old Carol :

> He came all so still
> There his mother was,
> As dew in April
> That falleth on the grass.

And what a long way that had come down the years, now into the blackout and to the " ghastly dew " that Tennyson saw which had fallen on and blasted the grass not far from where we were listening.

Well, after supper, we went into the hall again and this time had a free-and-easy impromptu concert. The three musicians played or sang whatever they fancied, and the soprano taught us to sing some rounds. We began with the obvious and easy ones, " Frère Jaques " and " Three Blind Mice," and then went soaring up to things more elaborate. My favourite—and indeed it was everybody's favourite, and somebody is likely to be overheard singing it along one of the corridors as long as the hostel remains—was the one about the swan singing " Tirralayo." (The spelling here is guess-work.) You start low in " The Swan sings " and then you

swoop up, not too jerkily, to " Tirra———" and then come down
in lovely lazy curves on "—layo, Tirralayo, Tirralayo." We
were shown how to sing it all together first, and then divided
into sections, to do the round properly. In a minute or two
the hall was filled with singing swans, and a melting perspective of tirralayos. You could see a vista of birds floating on
dream rivers. One curve of women's voices followed another.
It was enchanting. It was magic.

I wish you could have seen us as well as heard us. The high
hall, which looked older and more imposing in the firelight
than it does in daytime, and really might almost have passed
for something baronial; the pretty, flushed, smiling soprano
standing there conducting us; and then the semicircle of
women's and girls' faces—the evacuated mothers from Poplar,
Bootle, and the rest, nurses and nursery school students—all
wearing that wide innocent look which ordinary folk wear
when they are singing. And soaring from the firelight into
the blue of some fairytale country went the singing dream
swans, flashing a white wing then vanishing into the haze of
some eternal summer afternoon. Nothing I had seen, heard,
read, imagined, those many months, stirred me more deeply.
I tell you it was magic.

Now, let us take a look at the ingredients of this magic. The
chief one, you may well say, was the tune itself, or the fruitful
little marriage of tune and words in this particular round.
That I grant you, but let us see how it came to be sung in that
place by these five-and-twenty people. The house had been
requisitioned by the Ministry of Health to be a hostel for
women and tiny children from some of the poorest quarters
of our cities. What had housed before a few of the leisurely rich
was now the setting for an experiment in communal living
for the wives and babies of poor men. And all this was not
even imagined five years ago, except of course as part of
rumours from Russia. Then again, not only were these folk
set down in the distant countryside, not only were their toddlers

running in and out of former dining-rooms and libraries and rollicking in what were once secluded gardens, but also music, real music, made by professional musicians paid out of public funds, was being brought to them, to their evident enjoyment. If you had said to this excellent violinist five years ago : " Soon you will be travelling through pitch darkness to remote parts of Herefordshire to play Bach in the country houses to women from Poplar, Bootle, Salford," he would have thought you were out of your wits. And not only has it happened, but, as we have seen, it was magical when it happened.

This leads to two important conclusions. The first is the more obvious. People like me who, for many good reasons, have been much given during this war to talking about the new world we can create—and indeed *must* create—after the war, are often jeered at by those (and there are too many) who fear and hate all change, for deluding the people with our idle dreams. Stern reality, they tell us, will soon make short work of all our pretty fancies. And the answer is—this new world we talk about is not some future possibility but is already arriving. Sometimes we are already living in it. We were certainly all living in it while we were singing the round about the swans. For nothing in that whole scene made sense, could possibly be real, in the pre-war England or any direct continuation of it. Neither the audience nor the musicians could have been there. What probably would have been there were four elderly people yawning over a bridge table, and five or six servants chattering or moping in the kitchen. That was Old England in these parts. This was a bit of New England in these parts. We are changing—and changing rapidly—as we go along, and the very people who refuse to listen to any talk of a new world are actually seeing it set up almost under their noses. Why don't they notice the change? Because they think in terms of melodrama. They see the new world as a confused nightmare of red-shirted commissars, looted palaces, drunken fishwives elbowing frail old duchesses into the gutter, and masters of foxhounds chased like foxes. They do not realize that already the scenery is being shifted and a new cast waiting in the wings.

The second conclusion is perhaps even more important. Some people who admit that a new world is on its way are very grumpy about it, not because they fear a loss of power and privilege but because they are afraid there will not be much more fun. They foresee a bleak and priggish era. They have a sombre vision of herds of dull-eyed citizens being shepherded in and out of giant factories, and in and out of hostels and the like. Thus, women with young children might be sent to live in hostels that were formerly country mansions. Thus, there may be little groups of salaried government entertainers sent round to amuse these miserable herded exiles. But wait—are we talking about our concert that night? Because if we are, I must declare once more that the swans sang "Tirralayo" and that magic came through. And there is more than that to be said.

No peacetime, not following utter defeat, could offer so grim and narrowing an edge of life as that time of war, when you must remember our great creative efforts were being made not to provide the people with houses, restaurants, schools, hospitals, theatres, and the like, with good food, arts and crafts, holidays, and the like, but to provide ourselves and our allies with tanks, war planes, guns, and ammunition. What we were doing then in the way of new world improvisation was a mere hasty bit of work, a tiny side-show in the blackout.

Switch over the main creative effort to peacetime reconstruction, the whole community bent on building its new world, and then see what we can do. Yet even then, with the edge of life narrowing in the darkness, with the war cutting deeply into all our resources, with anxiety and worry gnawing away at us all, with everything against the moment flowering, *the magic came through*. Yes, the swans sang "Tirralayo." And I know now what this was the swan song of, what they

were singing clean out of the world, namely, all those cries,
" It can't be done " and " It shan't be done " and " Nobody
really wants it." For we know better, we who were there and
sang " Tirralayo."

F. Tennyson Jesse

A TALE OF ST. PETER'S GATE
Arnhem 1586–1944

ST. PETER stood at his gleaming Gate
Wondering what should be the fate
Of these muddy men who laughed like sin
And crowded the Gate and peered within
Blood-stained men who had fought their best
And now stormed heaven with careless jest.
" Oh, Peter, we didn't win—we died . . .
But when cocks crowed no man denied
The cause for which we all of us fought
So open the Gate—you damn well ought."
Then out came a man with a song on his lip
And a wound that shone like a star on his hip.
In his hand he carried a soldier's cup
And he stayed his song and he spoke up.
" Let them in, oh Peter, for these are *my* men,
Like me they fought and died at Arnhem ! "
And then the voices of Hollanders said :
" They fought for us, we too are dead
We also perished in farms and dykes
Not only when Sidney's men held pikes
But we true Dutch—men, women, and children
Helped and died with these Englishmen."
Sir Philip lifted his cup and said :
" These men will live, though they be dead !
They came from heaven in newest fashion
But just as mine were their pain and passion."
So Peter opened the Gate and bowed,
And Sir Philip Sidney sang aloud :
" They came from the skies and they're here again
Oh, men of Arnhem, be free from pain ! "

Margaret Kennedy

THE MOTHERS

LATONA:

BANISHED from heaven, on earth I may not find
   A place of refuge for my body's pain.
Oh Delos, gentle isle, to me be kind
   Nor drive me to the heavy seas again!
Hid in thine olives, let me stay my quest
   Till I have borne the golden fruit of heaven.

THE SERPENT:

   No more, no more, oh Woman unforgiven
   Shall you have rest!

       The Woman I fear
       The Woman must die.
       Lest she bear One
       Who is greater than I.

       I drive and torment her
       With anguish and dread.
       For the Son of the Woman
       Shall bruise my old head.

       I have conquered the earth
       For a day and a night
       The Woman I fear:
       She carries the Light.

> Far she shall wander
> In peril and scorn.
> The Son of the Woman
> Shall never be born.

MARY :

> There was no room for me. From door to door
>   He drove me, hapless, down the bitter years.

LATONA :

> A mountain billow casts me on the shore!
>   Twixt sea and land the God of Light appears.

MARY :

> From house to barn, from barn to byre he drove.
>   A stable hides the anguish and the danger.
>   I bear, I live, I cradle in a manger
> The God of Love.

EVE :

>> Smite ancient foe!
>> Primordial Wrong!
>> Many my daughters,
>> Cunning and strong.

>> How shall you find her
>> Who carries your fate
>> The queen in the tower,
>> The thrall at the gate,

>> Goddess or Maiden,
>> Peasant or slave?
>> Who bears the Valiant,
>> Appointed to save?

Seek her and find her,
Smite her—and then
Bow to the mighty
Redeemer of men.

James Lansdale Hodson

ARGUMENT AT POST 'W'

"THE question is—Is Harry out of the fashion? This makes four, doesn't it, Harry?" Mr. Stack took off his steel helmet and placed it upside down on the wooden floor. Being Chief Warden he was almost by right in the chair. He wore Pip, Squeak and Wilfred, the ribbons of the last war, on his blue battle-dress. Moreover, he was a retired solicitor. In Post W he carried weight. Pernickety, people granted that, a little pompous perhaps, but still . . .

Harry Makepeace said with feeling, and wondering what on earth old Stack had again asked if it made four for, since he had told them that already, that it certainly made four all right and whether he was out o' fashion or not, he certainly looked like being out o' pocket since this one would cost about twice as much as the first one. "We'd sold the pram, too," he said. "Didn't bargain for another." The Fates, Harry seemed to say, had been too much for him.

"Too bad, too bad," said Mr. Stack, but his mind wasn't on that. "The point is, Is Harry out of the fashion? Nathan Shakeshaft said he was."

Nathan, the cobbler, looked over his spectacles and said: "That's what I said. What's the average, I say. How many *you* got, Mr. Stack?"

"One," said Mr. Stack primly. "A Major in the artillery." And he glanced round challengingly.

"And *you*, Jess?" said Nathan to Jess Mossop, who worked at the face in Flint pit.

"We'n had three," said Jess. "But young Wilf—he were

takken wi' whooping cough. And Jim—yo' know about Jim—a rear-gunner. So we've only Mary, like, now." There was a pause.

Mr. Stack cleared his throat. "Mr. Jones-Williams, do you——"

Mr. Jones-Williams, the draper, said : " I was going to say that Mr. Mossop made a point—a good point, too. Why haf people had so few children? Cannon fodder iss the answer, ladies and gentlemen, cannon fodder. Mr. Mossop, he——"

" I said nowt o' the sort," said Jess, not liking this at all. He added bluntly : " If you must know, it weren't talk about war stopped us havin' any more, it were—well, our doctor said she mustn't. It seems somethin' had gone wrong when Mary come."

Harry Makepeace had been fidgeting. It was his fourth had started all this. Harry, a loom tackler, was used to arguments. He said : " When I said we didn't bargain for another, that's true enough. But once it's here—that's different. What did that poet say—' Tha'rt welcome, bonnie brid—tha shouldn't ha' come just when tha did, times are bad '—but once it were there it were welcome enough. And another thing —somebody's got to fight the wars, haven't they? And who's goin' to do it, if nobody has any childer? "

" That's right, is that," said Jess.

" A nation's wealth lies in its citizens," said Mr. Stack, putting the tips of his fingers together.

" If that iss so," said Mr. Jones-Williams truculently, " what are we doing as a nation to see that they are porn in the right houses, tell me that." He looked round.

" Born in the right houses? " said Jess. " What's wrong wi' my house? "

Two or three now spoke at once—Miss Blanche Higgins, the vicar's sister; and a man with a drooping moustache deeply stained with nicotine who wore a pair of eyeglasses dangling on his loose waistcoat. This was Mr. William Johnson who edited the *Weekly Examiner*. He had stopped abruptly and waved on Miss Higgins. Miss Higgins, a small lady with a Roman nose who had once stood as a Liberal parliamentary candidate and failed, said: "Family allowances will solve many of the problems, I'm sure. It's a sound principle in the armed forces. It's equally sound for civil life." She smiled at Mr. Johnson. "That's all I wanted to say."

Mr. Johnson bowed to her. He lit a new cigarette from the stump of the old one. No hurrying Mr. Johnson. He said: "I w-went into this question some time ago." He paused there and puffed his cigarette. "It o-occurred to me just before the war that if we—if we went on as we were, Hitler would have no need to fi-fight us—the country would be handed to him—to him on a plate because, because there would soon be nobody left to—left to defend it."

"Come," said Mr. Stack benevolently, "not quite so bad as that, Mr. Johnson, not *quite* so bad."

"Worse," said Mr. Johnson, "worse. Rapidly—rapidly becoming a nation of old men and young children and with the fe-feeble-minded the most prolif-prolific."

Harry Makepeace frowned and knocked out his pipe.

"That's why we have to have family allowances," said Miss Higgins brightly.

Mr. Johnson went on inexorably, but slowly. "I spent some hours one—one afternoon studying *Who's Who* to see how many children our bet-betters possess—our High Court Judges, our Cabinet Ministers, our B-Bishops and—and so on. They average about one and a bit. So they are not repro-reproducing themselves. I wrote an article setting all this out but—but it wasn't published."

"Ah!" said Miss Higgins, whose opinion of the Press was very low.

"Libellous?" inquired Mr. Stack, wisely.

"Oh no," said Mr. Johnson. "Oh no. But as my proprietor has only one son and he's no cr-credit to him, and as I have none at all, our posi-position was not remarkably strong. No, not strong at all. Mind you, that doesn't prevent us expressing our views as a—as a rule, but here—a little delicate."

"Children run in families," said Harry Makepeace stubbornly. "Some has 'em and some hasn't. I were the youngest o' seven."

"Seventh son of the seventh son, Harry?" inquired Mr. Stack. "He's said to be a genius."

"That's what I say," said Nathan. "The Almighty plays Himself in—when He's made two or three in one family, He gets His hand in—they improve. It shouldn't be the first son as inherits—it should be the last."

"Would you—you say that's why the world is in such a mess, Nathan?" inquired Mr. Johnson.

"Shouldn't be a bit surprised," said Nathan cheerfully. He began to feel he had uttered a really staggering idea—revolutionary.

"The bastards of history have often been m-men of brains," said Mr. Johnson casually, lighting another cigarette from the stump of the old one.

Mr. Stack cleared his throat again. He had always felt, coming from the south, that these north countrymen were excessively blunt. He said: "I suppose there's something in the preference for a baby motor-car over a baby—those who felt they couldn't afford both, have bought a car." That ought to get the discussion on firmer ground, he thought. But Mr. Johnson was off again. He said: "I would like to—to pursue Nathan's idea but on another line. It may—may well be that some of the cleverest children are at the—at the tail end. But what is—what is equally lamentable is what I had noted myself—the failure of brilliant men and women to have children at all. Bernard Shaw. No progeny. If I were a Dictator—I should try to—try to persuade such a citizen not to die childless. There might be many a charming woman quite ready . . ."

Mr. Stack looked round to see if anybody else was as surprised and shocked as he was. They didn't appear to be. Miss Higgins was sitting forward on her chair and spoke at once. " You attach too much importance to parentage, Mr. Johnson," she said. " You'd be astonished how many High Court Judges—or men of that sort—have produced mental deficients. Environment is the important thing. Good houses, good education, good food—and the supply of first-class brains will be doubled."

Mr. Jones-Williams said : " When I preed my terriers, it's the dog and pitch that counts most—not the kennel they're porn in. Why should it be different with humans, tell me that."

Mr. Stack, pouring on his oil, said : " Something in both, no doubt. Breeding takes time. One generation isn't usually enough."

Nathan pushed his moustache aside with the stem of his pipe. " I'd like to know," he said, " what Mr. Johnson has to say about this. I've got a daughter whose young man were killed at Dunkirk. She's never had another. Maybe she never will have. Young men are going to be in what the papers call ' short supply '. She's very fond o' childer. If she never has one, she'll be heart-broken."

Nobody spoke for a moment or two. Then Miss Higgins said softly : " There were thousands like her after the last war." She moved a hand over her brow. She said, but it was difficult to hear it : " I was one myself. "

Mr. Johnson said, fiddling with his eyeglasses : " I recollect a piece I wrote about the l-lost generation and the price women were paying as—as well as men. I said if you destroy young men you destroy—or half destroy your young women. I said, ' Has society no suggestions to m-make, no solution to offer? ' Must so many of our finest women remain childless? "

" And did anybody make any? " asked Miss Higgins gently.

" Oh, no," said Mr. Johnson. " None at all. We g-got a number of letters from readers saying—saying if we published anything further on that line they would cease to—cease to take the paper. My proprietor was most upset—whether by the article or the letters I was never—never quite sure."

"Well," said Mr. Stack with an air of winding it up, "it's a very large subject—very large indeed."

But the wardens were not finished yet.

"If Hitler had had six kids," said Harry Makepeace, "there'd never ha' been this war at all. Imagine it—six kids ready to go into the army—and then startin' a war. No man would ever do it."

"His wife would never have let him," said Nathan. He smoothed his moustache. "I know mine wouldn't."

"It comes back to what I said pefore," said Mr. Jones-Williams, his eye lighting up. "You must have the children porn in the right houses. Stands to sense that if the governing classes who decide on wars haf no children and the children who do most fighting come from the poorest houses—well, there iss not the brake on wars there would otherwise pe."

"Come, come," said Mr. Stack. "Everybody knows how many of the nobility are always killed in war. They're among the first to go. They're *professionals* at war-making."

"So much the worse," said Mr. Jones-Williams. "Put am I right, Mr. Johnson? When you ran that feature about families with most children serving and some had five sons, where did they come from?"

"Well," said Mr. Johnson, "they certainly came mostly from the people with the least m-money. There's no doubt where—where the children are born. Show me an abundance of poverty and slums—and there—and there I'll show you an abundance of children. Miss Higgins's work has proved that to her, I th-think."

Miss Higgins nodded. She said: "We all want security of employment, we all want better wages and conditions—but unless this question of children is right, nothing is right."

Mr. Jones-Williams was still smouldering. He said: "There

iss a song, iss there not, which says I didn't pring up my boy Albert to pe eaten by a lion in the Tower at Blackpool. Well, I did not pring up my children to pe eaten by the lion of war. Unless you stop war, nothing iss right—nothing whateffer."

Harry Makepeace shook his head. " It's no good talking that road," he said. " That's just giving in before you start. If nobody has kids because this is a wicked world, well—who's going to make it better? No, that's no good at all. If we'd had no British lads to fight Hitler's lot, why, the world would have been in a terrible state by this time."

" It iss terrible now," said Mr. Jones-Williams.

" It's terrible," said Nathan, " but it would ha' been a sight worse. As it is, it'll start improving."

" If it doesn't," said Jess Mossop, " I shall wonder what our Jim died for." There was silence again.

Mr. Johnson took out another cigarette from its paper packet and his hand trembled a little. He said : " Your Jim, Jess, died —for us here. For—for me in a way more than you—because— because I had no son to stand beside him. I feel that—very much."

He took a long, deep breath and let it go again. " We live in a—in a world where many countries do not—not hold life sacred as we do. There are large—large areas in the world where life is—is cheap, where barbarism and torture flourish, and justice is hardly known. How is all that to be put right? What a task it is, what a task." He fell silent.

Harry Makepeace shook himself. " It'll not be done by having no childer—not if I'm any judge," he said. He looked round. Mr. Stack said, nodding his head to the words : "Happy is the man that hath his quiver full of them."

Nathan was tempted to ask him a personal question. But he didn't. He said : " Sounds to me like putting the clock back—aye, and putting you into fashion after all, Harry."

This was too good an opportunity for Mr. Stack to miss. He grabbed his hat and got on his feet.

Reginald Reynolds

"CHILDREN WERE AMONG THE CASUALTIES..."

BRIGHT was the frosted road, and bright
    The star that was our guide,
But sad the heart that sought the light
    On that grim Christmastide,
For there, on that December night
    The innocents had died.

If there were manger, stall or inn
    There was no sign to show,
Or that those children were the kin
    Of Christ. I only know
The gutted homes that blindly grin
    Like skulls, set in a row.

But I, remembering, will see
    The fires of hell burn red
And a solitary, blasted tree
    That glowed, as though it bled,
A thing of loveliness to me,
    Of life, among the dead.

O Calvary of sudden bliss,
    O Christmas tree of pain—
For bitter comfort born of this,
    Christ, Thou hast died again,
And pierced my heart with Abel's kiss
    Upon the lips of Cain.

Lord Dunsany

FÜHRERS AND KIPPERS

HOWEVER easily writers may appear to write, in reality they need their material just as urgently as the cook needs hers when cooking a hare, according to the famous recipe. The writer's material is an idea, and, whether it be provided by chance or by long brooding, the idea has to be come by before any writer can do anything. The shock that stimulated the idea with which I began this short article was when I read that a primary object of this book would be to spread an appreciation . . . of the family as a unit of society. I had often dimly feared that the spread of an appreciation of this was becoming necessary, but it was a shock to see it in cold type. I had feared it when, some years after hearing that children and dogs were not allowed in flats, I noticed that vast numbers of flats were being built, and that the flat was obviously becoming a national institution. Not only in towns, which are bad places for children in any case, but far out in the country, these great buildings were rising up, and in many of them (I do not know how many) there was this little curse in the contract. Now, wherever I see anything wrong, I gaze, however shortsightedly, however dimly, but as far as I can, into the future, to see what it is likely to lead to. And, even when I cannot see what any evil is likely to lead to, I am quite convinced that every evil will either be overthrown or will drag down those who uphold it. There are several cures for evils; none of them pleasant. The Black Death, for instance, checked bad sanitation. But the cure that history usually sends us is war. Many may think that a clause in a number of contracts forbidding children could have no effect so far-reaching as war. I, on the other hand, never see any evil without seeing the shadow of war loom up through the ages. The reason for this view that I take is that, while nearly everyone else appears to be seeking perpetual peace by tying up the Nazis by some treaty that, unlike the one at Versailles, will be binding upon them, I believe that the wolf is always at the door, waiting to take advantage of any folly, weakness or rottenness, and that he roams the world in such numbers that, though he be Hitler to-day, there will be plenty more of him when Hitler is dead, always waiting to run in at our door when we leave it unbolted, or to push his way through the timbers when any of them are rotten. Nor do I believe that any form of government whatever will bring peace to the world; in fact I do not believe in perpetual peace at all: it never has been until our time, and we were so clever that we invented a scheme twenty-five years ago that should accomplish what the ages were unable to do, but we only deluged the world in blood. No doubt there will be many more schemes, and even the old one may be dragged out again, but, as I do not believe we can prevent war, I see only one thing that we can guard against, and that is defeat. As we were not defeated in 1914 or 1940, when our preparations, if any, were so inadequate, we may well hope to guard against being defeated ever. We have given defeat every chance, by leaving the navy without adequate ships, because we believed the League of Nations was going to prevent war, and by such follies in 1914 that a suggestion that the artillery should have adequate shells was hailed as a profound and brilliant policy. But it is not enough to suggest that the fleet should have ships, and the artillery shells: one should look into the causes why a people made these two blunders, and, though we are not likely to repeat those two follies, yet if the causes of them are there we shall make others as bad. Therefore whether Hitler should be hanged or shot always seemed to me only a trifle. To safeguard our future we should go down to our own foundations and see that they are sound. Something would seem to

be wrong somewhere if there is any need for the appreciation
of the family as the unit of society. Let us look as the woodman
in a northern forest would look at the timbers and the bolts
of his door, though a wolf was not visible at the moment,
yet knowing that the forest was full of them, and that they
creep close before they are seen. I am afraid we shall find plenty
of things that are wrong, as the woodman might find plenty
of specks of decay in his door, and, if an evil star shines on
him, he may say : " Those little specks don't matter : they are
nothing."

Let us take one of those harmless specks of decay in our
civilization, too small to notice, too ludicrous to mention, but
containing the seeds of death : let us take, for instance, kippered
herrings. It may seem trivial or ludicrous that we can no longer
get a kippered herring, so far as I know, in all England. They
dye them instead. But look at the evil until it ceases to seem
funny, and see if there is nothing wrong with our system,
which permits the public to be cheated with dyed herrings that
have creosote poured over them instead of being prepared in the
old way. I am not going over every speck of decay in our door,
and it should be enough to point out two. Some while ago
a child drank poison and died : it came out at the inquest
that his father kept the poison for mishandling the herrings
that he sold. He said that, much to his regret, he had left
the bottle of poison on too low a shelf, where his child was
able to get it. The coroner pointed out he should not have
done so; but neither the coroner, nor the Press, nor anybody
but I, ever suggested that this man should not have put the
poison where the public could get it. Some years ago there
was a terrible outbreak of poisoning among children. It was
traced to a confectioner, who said that greatly to his regret
he had unfortunately mistaken his sack of arsenic for his sack
of powdered chalk; and, the dose of powdered chalk being
far the larger of the two, the children had their dose of arsenic
for what should have been their dose of chalk. However

much his mistake was criticized I never heard it suggested that either of these commodities should not have been used for manufacturing sweets. Anyone who criticizes such things is always called a food-faddist, as though creosote and powdered chalk were natural and right, while wholesome fish and honest sugar were something too intricate and fanciful for ordinary people. I think it is evils like these in our midst, rotting our strength morally as well as physically, that are as likely to be a source of future wars as are the vagaries of foreign dictators.

THE QUAY

Anna Hook

James Bridie

FAR AND FEW

FAR away, and the farther the better, five Professors of a Northern University were trying to make a shrimp. They were called Mordred Anguish, Fantern Lee, James Loop, Hugh Horse and Job Dick. Their task may seem to you a strange one, but I am about to explain.

Anguish looked like a shaven llama. Loop looked like an egg on a post. Eggo was his nickname. Horse looked like a horse. These three were all tall men and Horse was the tallest. The smallest was Job Dick, a round man with a fluffy white beard. Between them came Professor Lee, a polished person who kept trying out expressions on his face, so that he had no sooner looked wise than he looked amiable and he had no sooner looked amiable than he looked stern and uncompromising. To keep himself fit he was often to be seen on roller skates, even in his laboratory. On roller skates he was the epitome of grace.

Above them all was Sir Fred Wombat. He was the Principal and Vice-Chancellor of the University. The Island on which the University was placed was mountainous, citied to the top, crowded, as Mr. Browning said, with culture. It was in the nearer Hebrides. The Principal's Lodging was a magnificent building at the very top. In it sat Principal Wombat smoking a hookah and thinking long, long thoughts. Once, when the University went on fire, the fireman came to save him and Lady Wombat.

" What, if one may ask, is the matter? " he asked the Fire-master.

"The University is in flames," answered that excellent man.

"Do you remember what Hikkypos said in 666 B.C.?" said Sir Fred.

"I can't say that I do," replied the Firemaster.

"He said, 'Amphi epi huper; paraperipros.'"

"And no doubt he was right," said the Firemaster. "This is the way to the fire escape."

That anecdote will show you at once what sort of a man was Sir Fred Wombat, so we need waste no more time on his learning, his nonchalance and his personal appearance, which was that of a largish potato, unpeeled and covered with knobs.

*   *   *

What, then, induced those five Professors to devote themselves to making a shrimp? Is it not that there are or were enough shrimps in the world. There cannot be too many of those interesting little creatures. Nothing looks at once so old and so young as a shrimp and I have yet to hear of its doing any harm to anybody whatever—at least, wittingly. It has no claws, like the lobster; and yet it has the delightful property of turning shell-pink and scarlet when it is boiled. One of the bravest old ladies I ever knew ate them, shells, whiskers and all by the handful, and she wore indifferently fitting false teeth in her upper and in her lower jaw. Even to her they were harmless. We cannot, I say, have too many shrimps. But it was not for that reason that the Professors set about making one.

Nor was it for the reason that they had little to do with their time. For many years the University had existed less and less on what the parents of its pupils paid for their education and more and more on the gifts of rich men whose yachts were forever anchoring softly in the harbour in the blue twilight.

The Bay was a pleasant anchorage, for the Gulf Stream floated into it, and such students as there were bathed with great delight far into October. The warm water on their skins made them gentle and tolerant and soft and lazy. If their Professors had not been almost as soft and lazy they would hardly have passed any examinations at all. As it was, more than one Professor used to put a heap of examination papers on his mantelpiece and, after looking at them sadly for some hours without opening the buff covers, would allot marks by the smell of them. At one viva voce examination for an honours degree, the University Beadle had to be sent for from his pub to wake up the candidate and the Board of Examiners, for they had all fallen asleep.

There was a Biological Station on the headland, Butt of the Buckies, and from this, on a fine summer day, a motor launch with a dredging apparatus used to drift about the warm bay lifting all manner of fish and old boots and tins from the depths of the sea. These discoveries were spread on the deck and bits of seaweed were separated from gravel, sand, orange peel, sand eels, drowned mariners and things on the broad deck of the research ship. One day they caught a King Crab.

A King Crab is an anachronism. An anachronism is a thing that has wandered into the wrong century. A King Crab is an extraordinary beast with a huge, hooded shell and horrible great claws. Such was Pau Amma, illustrated by Mr. Kipling in Mr. Kipling's story of Pau Amma. "China going P. and O.'s" you remember, "pass Pau Amma's playground close. And his Pusat Tasek lies in the tract of most B.I.s" It was strange that this King Crab should have got into the Gulf Stream and very interesting to the Professor of Biology who had, on the day when this Crab was dredged, taken his wife and children for a sail.

Be that as it may, there was the King Crab, walloping slowly about the deck, and there was the Professor of Biology staring at him through his spectacles and remembering that he had seen a picture of him once in one of the books he had read in the library when he was studying for his degree. He called his wife and children, and they came running.

o

"Look, my darlings, a King Crab," said the Professor.

"He is an anachronism," said the Professor.

"I don't like it," he added.

"Why don't you like it, father?" said little Chlamydomolas, the most clever of his children.

"For this reason," replied her father. "The King Crab is a predatory monster, very difficult to destroy, anachronism though he may be. It is because he is difficult to destroy that he survives in a Universe that has no place for him. Look at the strength of his carapace or shell."

With that he rapped the King Crab's shell sharply with a hammer and it gave forth a loud, dull note.

"The sea, and in particular this Bay, abounds with harmless floating and swimming things which illustrate my lectures and give comfort to the population when they take the form of what the Americans call Sea Food. Further inhabitants of these waters are yourselves, my dear children when, in seemly bathing costumes, you disport yourselves among the gentle waves. The arrival of this dread monster, if indeed he be, as I imagine, but the first of an army of similar monsters, is of ill omen for the local denizens of the deep. I do not like it. I shall raise the question of this at the next meeting of the Faculty."

He shook his head rapidly from side to side several times. What he was trying to say was that lots of King Crabs might well follow the first and ravage all Buckie Bay with their terrible biting nippers.

Clammy Anguish was a child of quick sympathy. Tears leaped to her eyes and she clasped her hands together with a wringing motion.

"O, Papa," said Clammy, "what will become of the little fish, the harmless little fish about which you wrote so beautifully in the *Encyclopædia Britannica*?"

"You refer, my child," said her father, "to my article on Innocuparvopiscatology. Since I wrote that, more years ago than I care to or even can remember, I have felt responsible for harmless little fish. Their sorrows are my sorrows, their joys my joys. If anything were to happen to them, I should hardly care to live."

He mingled his tears with those of his daughter and together they walked the plank on to the jetty and made their way up the steep hill road between its walls of blooming gorse. More than one wayfarer stopped to look at them, imagining that the rest of the family had met with a drowning accident or something, until they appeared round a bend at a lower level. Tears (or any overt expression of the emotions) were rare on the Island. Among the University Set they were not uncommon; but the University Set rather kept itself to itself, as the saying went. To see two of that Set walking up the Hill Road weeping was enough to excite talk in the Town and talk it did excite.

II

The Professors were exhausted. In spite of that they decided to work on for another hour after tea-time. There was no denying that the matter was urgent.

It is perhaps inaccurate to say that there was *no* denying. Doctor Lee, quite early in the proceedings and from time to time later, gesticulated with his features and suggested, mildly and always subject to correction, that, taking a long view, while admitting that there were reasonable indications for a certain amount of anxiety, it was doubtful whether there was complete occasion for panic measures, that there might even be grounds for a degree of quiet confidence.

This standpoint was readily countered by the white-hot enthusiasm of Professor Anguish. "I know," he said, "my King Crab. I also, as perhaps you will admit, know my duty. I do not presume to dictate, but it seems to me that the duty of all of us is plain and points to the hard road, the steep road."

"True, true, true, true," trilled Job Dick, whose pleasing

voice always reminded listeners of that of a linnet. "We must explore every avenue and leave no stone unturned. It is, as Mordred says, our duty."

"Stern daughter of the voice of God," said Hugh Horse.

"I beg your pardon?" said James Loop. . . .

So down they got to work again. The typists leapt like kittens to their keys. Technicians fiercely boiled up things in glass jugs, glared through microscopes, soused specimens in formaldehyde and rattled at their microtomes with sounds like sleigh bells. Through it all came the steady hum of the cerebrations of the Professors. It was a busy scene, and a noisy one too. The Gate Porter jangled his keys irritably, for it was five o'clock and an hour past locking-up time. Wombat, from his eyrie, wondered mildly what was toward.

"When," said Mordred Anguish, "we have made one shrimp, complete in its armour as Pallas Athene was when she was born from the skull of Zeus, it will be a simple matter to extend the process indefinitely. Loop has worked it out. If there is such a thing as Indefiniteness, our work may be extended to indefinite limits. We may arm effectively the tittlebat and the tadpole. We shall place an overwhelming restraint on the activities of the King Crab. But, above all things, let us be practical. Let us look the facts squarely in the face."

"As we have always tried to do," said Fantern Lee.

"I do you and us that justice," said Anguish.

"God bless you, old boy," said Lee, grasping his colleague warmly by the hand.

At this point the Porter came in carrying the Vice-Chancellor's compliments and suggestion that it was time the Laboratories closed for the night. As Sir Fred's word was law and as the Professors were very tired, closed they were.

III

It is not to be supposed that the energies of the Senatus were exclusively devoted to this scientific planning. Organization was essential and organization, heaped up and running over, was provided. Bathing machines were sternly regulated. The Bay became alive with chugging little boats painted crimson and blue (the University colours). All accessible fish were stamped with serial numbers in indelible purple ink. The Pier itself was " controlled ".

The first relaxation of these stern measures came with the Quinquennial Regatta. This Event was allowed to proceed as a concession to popular feeling and after long deliberation. There was no reason to regret the decision. It was a very enjoyable Regatta indeed—quite one of the best that had ever been held.

The next important event in the History of the University was the protracted discussion on the provision of bakelite buttons on the uniform of the Bedellus to replace the habitual brass ones. In this matter as in other matters, the University moved with the times.

Appendix

The Order of Merit was conferred on Sir Mordred Anguish, together with Permanent Honorary Corresponding Membership of the Brains Trust. His conclusion that it is impossible to *make* a shrimp in any practical connotation of the word " make ", ranks, of course, with Newton's Law of Gravitation, Einstein's Theory and the Ten Commandments.

Fantern Lee said to me, as we supported each other home from a Thump Supper, " Bridie," he said, " I once had high hopes of old Mordred. I thought we might make a Scientist of him. But you know how it is. Publicity has killed the reputation of many a better man than that dotty old idiot."

Phyllis Bottome

A CUP OF TEA

JANE EVEREST finished her review of her opponent's book with a sigh of relief. She glanced at the clock; it was not yet midnight when she could make her final round of the big mental hospital before going to bed. She was still on duty. As a neurologist she respected her opponent, but as a psychiatrist she felt that he had not so much gone astray as imprisoned himself in a hard shell of materialism. Roughly speaking he thought diseases or organic imperfections made people what they were and let them out of any necessity for improvement or any responsibility for defeat. He ignored the creative powers of the human being upon its own imperfect organs. "I don't say our patients" Jane thought to herself, "wholly make their own mental illnesses, but when you can reach them there is always something to call to besides the disease! They aren't really so condemned to solitary confinements as he thinks. There is a way out for all of them if one can only rouse them into wanting to take it!"

On one side of the medical quarters, where she had her own sitting-room and bedroom, were the wards of the male patients, upon the other the female. The doors between the hospital and the medical quarters were always left open at night. Partly to reassure the patients and partly so that there might be no delay in reaching the wards if there were any sudden calls.

But Jane did not expect any calls. The night sister, Job, was a particularly able woman, capable of dealing with any ordinary emergency likely to arise. The great troubled sea of minds in conflict was at rest. Jane's two juniors were out with a late pass. The superintendent was no doubt where he ought to be, in bed and asleep.

All the great buildings of the hospital were profoundly still. Jane took up a book to read, but though she opened it she found she could not read. She was still listening. The silence was no more complete than upon any other night but it had, to Jane's imagination, an odd quality of pressure. It was as if the silence were warning her to listen to it.

She must be very tired indeed, Jane told herself contemptuously if she could feel frightened. Only lay people suspect that dangerous things happen in mental hospitals. Doctors and their staffs see to it that no dangerous things can happen.

Jane had shut the window because of the fog, nothing moved outside in the dark garden, or inside in the bright sitting-room, except the occasional soft crunching noise of a displaced coal in the open fireplace.

It would, Jane thought, have been nice to have had a dog in the room but Jane had no dog. It would have been pleasant to have had even a cat, anything that felt comfortable and could make a sound would somehow or other have been welcome on this quiet night.

She must not, Jane reminded herself, go on listening, for the mere fact of concentrating all the senses into one, strained the nerves. She would make a plan, tidy the books on her shelf for instance, sew on a stray button, anything to make a little stir in this heavy pool of silence.

There was something so very like a sound at the door that Jane turned her eyes towards it. That was the kind of trick, Jane told herself impatiently, that her patients played upon themselves, they thought the handles of doors turned when there was no one to turn them. The only difference now was, that while Jane's patients imagined the handles were turning, this particular handle was really turning.

The door opened very slowly and cautiously, giving Jane plenty of time to tell herself first that it was the wind, secondly that there wasn't any wind, and thirdly that it couldn't be anything to make a fuss about. The door opened about six inches and then stopped as if the person on the other side of it were waiting to see who was in the room.

For a moment Jane was seized with panic; her forehead pricked with sweat, her throat turned dry. Even if she made a dash for the window there was nothing but fog and darkness to rush into. There was no other door and no hiding place. The bell was on the farther side of the door under the telephone. Then as suddenly as it came, her sense of panic retreated. "I am in charge of this hospital," Jane said to herself firmly, and picking up her white linen coat which lay beside her ready for her night rounds she slipped it on. She felt still less afraid after she had it on. "Come in," she said, in gentle cheerful tones, and six foot two of homicidal maniac slouched into the room.

All along Jane had been afraid it would be "Jerry"; and it was Jerry. He was a jet-black negro suffering from paranoia. He had already murdered three women; murder was in fact his main reaction to women. His huge black paws moved restlessly in front of him, as if they were already feeling for the wind-pipe it was his favourite method to crush. His white eyeballs rolled horribly and his breath came like a man running. All his thoughts and his movements were congealed into one set purpose. Jerry was a killer; and he was out to kill.

Jane looked across the room at the huge shambling ape of a man summing up her chances. She knew that they were extremely small. "If I am going to die," she said to herself, "I may as well try to understand a little about it first."

"What is the matter, Jerry?" Jane asked aloud, her eyes fixed steadily upon him and wholly without hostility. "Hadn't you better sit down, in that comfortable arm-chair over there, and tell me all about it?"

Jerry stopped his wavering advance. His rolling eyeballs sank away from Jane. He looked confusedly about him at the delicate objects of her sitting-room as if he were making up his mind which to start tearing up first. Jane could almost see his thoughts moving behind the great furrowed forehead. He had no freedom of choice. He was being pushed violently towards physical destruction, but until he actually began to destroy there was just a margin of safety.

The cords in his temples stood out like black ropes and his hands fumbled as if he already felt between them the objects he was going to strip and tear.

He seemed, however, to have heard what Jane said, for he shuffled towards the chair and sank down into it. His great splay feet were bare. He wore only the flannel pyjamas he had escaped in, they were open at the throat showing his heavy hairy chest.

" Now tell me what is wrong? " Jane repeated encouragingly. She chose her words with care, speaking them slowly, with little pauses between them. This was partly because of the physical sickness of terror which she had to control in herself and partly in order to reach, through the confusion of Jerry's fury, the big simple negro, whom she had always treated as her friend.

He had heard her, or he would not have sat down. Something had superimposed itself already upon his one bleak aim. Jane had not changed his purpose but she had for the moment succeeded in postponing the cruel sense of hurry and pressure that is the accompaniment of all mental instability.

Jerry glared across the three yards that separated them, as if he were trying to pump up afresh in himself the maniac ecstasy. " Ise gwine to kill you all! " he shouted at her. " Ise gwine ter do you-all in! "

" Tell me first what has upset you? " Jane demanded. " You are my friend, Jerry, and I have always been your friend, you know very well that I have never done you any harm! "

Jerry shuffled his feet and raised his voice higher and higher, as if to shout down any remnant of opposition in his own mind. "Maybe I's a black man," he cried. "I shorely am! But why the hell can't I'se have my cup o' tea jes like any onory white man! Why mus' I'se be served las'? I'se tell you-all Doc! I'se ain't had no sugar in my second cup! I'se ain't gwine to stand it. I'se gwine ter do you-all in! You-all is the Boss!"

Jerry moved his chair nearer; he was in reach now of Jane's small neat figure. His wild eyes were on the pulse that leaped in her throat.

Jane sat erect and still. "They served you last did they?" she repeated quietly. "Well, you have to take your turn, Jerry, perhaps to-morrow they will serve you first, you wouldn't think that unfair would you? If they forgot to give you sugar in your second cup I will tell them to-morrow that they must never forget to give it to you again."

"I'se ain't never had 'nuff sugar!" Jerry shouted. "It's clarrs warfare that's what it is! I ain't never had 'nuff sugar since I'se been yare!"

"Well," Jane said consideringly, "if you haven't had enough sugar, Jerry, how would you like me to give you some tea now?" Jane watched his rolling eyes, they seemed hooded against thought. But her words had stirred something in him, a vague response to her kindness rose and battled against the clenched antagonism that gripped him fast.

It was as if a thread of consciousness separated itself from the bulk of his obsession. "If you-all try to fool me I'se gwine to kill you-all," he told her gruffly.

"I shan't need to leave the room," Jane answered reassuringly. "I often make my own tea here. I will show you where I keep my things. I boil my water here in an electric kettle and I keep everything else in a cupboard. The water I get from the tap behind this little curtain."

Jane rose very slowly, and looked down at Jerry with a kindly smile. She did not know how she managed this smile, but in her heart there was quite as much pity as there was fear. Perhaps there was even more pity for this poor angry child caught in the trap of his own fury. Resentment and self-pity so filled him to the brim that he had no room for anything beyond his own self-torment.

Even under the shadow of an awful death Jane knew that she had something else in her besides her personal terror.

While she moved about the room Jerry shouted defiant and indecent things at her, but he did not try to stop her.

She produced her teapot and silver canister and wheeled a tray, which she kept ready in order to make tea for herself and her colleagues, close to Jerry's chair.

When she had to turn her back on him, she shut off from her mind anything but her tea-making. She told him beforehand, each thing she was going to do so that he might feel some share in her actions; and by sharing, divert his fixed intent further and further from its goal.

" Now Jerry," Jane said at last, " you must watch the water in the kettle, first it will sing a little, then the cover will begin to move because there will be bubbles underneath it, and then we shall know the water is ready for us to make tea with! But we must be patient for they say ' a watched pot never boils '."

When she had made every preparation that she could think of Jane went back to her chair while Jerry watched her suspiciously. If she had not gone back to the same chair he would have been, Jane knew, more suspicious still. She noticed that the swollen ropes on his forehead had decreased in size. He told her over and over again, the story of how he had been cheated at tea-time, but with decreasing fury. The waves of his anger rose and fell like the lessening waves of a retreating tide.

" I suppose all his life," Jane thought to herself, " he has been without something that he thought he ought to have had! He has not lived as an equal among his own people. No doubt white people have teased him and made him feel isolated. Women too perhaps have injured his male pride, to be scorned by white women must have felt fearfully degrading to all that splendid strength! He must have felt himself and all his powers fruitless and wasted. He might have been a good simple man if he had been respected and felt at home in the world."

His eyes had left her now; they watched the kettle, with the simple eagerness of a child. Jane left it entirely to him. He was the first to observe the faint sound of the water before it came to the boil, and when the cover moved, he shouted with delight. "We must go slowly," Jane reminded him. "Take off that contact first! Yes—like that! and here is the tea-pot. I have already warmed it, and now you have only to pour the water over the tea. To drink it really good and strong we must wait three minutes more. Here is the clock, please time it for me!"

Was she trying to fool him? Once more Jerry shot a glance at her, dark with suspicion. Should he not make quite sure by killing her first now before he had his tea? Suppose someone should come in and prevent him! Jane almost saw the thoughts in his great empty mind. She said, "There is no hurry. No one will come in." Then she put, very slowly so that he could count them, four lumps of sugar in his tea. "Now," Jane said, "try it, and if it is not sweet enough you shall have some more. Stir it first with this little spoon!" A slow grin spread over the dark tortured face. The great furrows in Jerry's brow smoothed themselves out, slowly he raised the delicate egg-shell china to his thick lips. The tea was strong enough. It was sweet enough. He had been helped first. He drank four cups, then Jane said gently, "Now Jerry, you must go back to bed; but if you like, just to be on the safe side, you can take the sugar-basin with you!"

Jerry hesitated, glared at her and got up. Jane, too, rose to her feet with the sugar-basin in her hand and held it out to him. "I will come with you," she said gently, "just to see that you get safely back without being scolded!"

Would his purpose swing back, with this new action? Was all that had come between him and his murderous impulse—

the sense of their comradeship over an accepted task—the friendliness and achieved purpose—to be lost and wasted?

Jane thought first of this. The sense of her own danger had receded until it had ceased to be a part of her consciousness; but not for a moment had her desire to help Jerry decreased, on the contrary it had grown, until it had swallowed up all other thoughts. He must not be allowed to hurt himself against his own anger, he must be got safely out of his obsession, into a region where his eager simplicity might have a harmless vent.

Jane went with him to the door but she let him open it.

They met no one in the long wide corridors. They walked in silence side by side, Jerry carrying the little silver sugar-basin as reverently as if it were a religious symbol. Jane's fair head barely reached to his elbow.

They met Sister Job outside the door of the ward for the fractious male patients. She had discovered what had happened and faced them, chalk-white and swaying where she stood.

" Jerry has come back," Jane said before they reached her. " He has been to my room to tell me that something unfair had happened to him. Sister Job only looks after you at night, Jerry, she did not know that you hadn't enough sugar, did you Sister? "

" No," whispered Sister Job, unlocking the door and locking it again after Jerry. The two women looked at each other for a long moment. All that both of them knew might have happened was in their haunted eyes.

" It's all right," Jane said at last. " Quite all right, Sister Job. I know very well it wasn't your fault! We'll find out all about it to-morrow——" It was curious how her physical strength suddenly began to fail her. The relief was too great! She was going to go on living, clean and safe, free from that overwhelming force of ugliness and hate; and she was not only free from poor black Jerry. She knew now for certain that she had been right. " He saved himself!" Jane thought proudly. " When I reached him! He pulled himself back! There is a last word that a man can always say to himself even against murder!"

Jane drew a deep breath, she wasn't going to faint but she was glad of Sister Job's sudden grip upon her arm. "You'd better come into my office, doctor," Sister Job said anxiously, "and have a cup of tea."

Viola Meynell

THE INFANT

HE tells his dreams, lifting his head in bed :
　" You were there with me, mother, and you said—'
" You and I raced together—you were last."
" I dreamt I hurt myself, but you went past."
" Some men attacked us, but you made them fly."
" No one was in the world but you and I."

All day I answer for my mood, my whim,
And put myself in shape to show to him.
But all the night God knows what I will do!
At eve we play and kiss, but I know, too,
Tucking him in with smiles before we part,
That before morning I may break his heart.

FROM the days of Scipio Africanus comes the story of his daughter Cornelia who, to a lady vaingloriously boasting of her precious stones, brought forward her sons, saying " These are my jewels." This is the spirit which has inspired the contributors to this book. And the whole nation agrees; politicians, scientists, poets and the people unite in investing their hope and faith in the future generations.

In 1790 Dr. Charles White, a name famous in the annals of British medicine, with a few forward-looking colleagues, founded Saint Mary's Hospitals in Manchester so that a more enlightened outlook could be brought to bear on the needs of mothers and children. After a hundred and fifty years these hospitals still minister to a wide and thickly populated area; about half a million babies have been born under their care and some nine thousand in-patients are treated annually.

Saint Mary's constitute the largest combined maternity and gynaecological hospital in the country, an unrivalled field of medical research, closely associated with the Manchester University. From this centre a constant procession of young doctors and trained nurses and midwives goes out into the world in the service of mothers and babies.

The Hospital has plans for the future, it is pledged to go forward—and this means money; and money given freely by those who believe that there is a margin of individual enterprise and free pioneer spirit wherein lies the value of a voluntary hospital. There are beds to be endowed—names to be remembered immortally. Will you add a page to this book by sending a gift according to your ability to the *Honorary Treasurer, Saint Mary's Hospitals, Manchester,* 13